Algae and Fungi

The left-hand side of the cover photo is of *Volvox aureus,* a motile colonial green alga. The right-hand side is of *Schizophyllum commune.* [Right-hand photo courtesy of Mrs. Ruth Allen.]

Initial Volumes in This Series

Algae and Fungi
C. J. Alexopoulos and H. C. Bold, The University of Texas

Ecology of Populations
Arthur S. Boughey, University of California, Irvine

Sensory Mechanisms
James Case, University of California, Santa Barbara

Integral Animal Behavior
David E. Davis, North Carolina State University

Molecular Genetics
A. Gib DeBusk, The Florida State University

Biology of Higher Cryptogams
William T. Doyle, University of California, Santa Cruz

Viruses and Molecular Biology
Dean Fraser, Indiana University

Hormonal Control in Vertebrates
B. E. Frye, The University of Michigan

Cells and Energy
Richard A. Goldsby, Yale University

The Physiology of Cells
Karl F. Guthe, The University of Michigan

Process and Pattern in Evolution
Terrell H. Hamilton, The University of Texas

Tools of Biology
Edward S. Lenhoff, Harvard University

A Biology of Higher Invertebrates
W. D. Russell-Hunter, Syracuse University

A Biology of Lower Invertebrates
W. D. Russell-Hunter, Syracuse University

Animal Morphogenesis
John W. Saunders, Jr., State University of New York, Albany

Evolution and Systematics
Otto T. Solbrig, The University of Michigan

Development in Flowering Plants
John G. Torrey, Harvard University

Principles of Development and Differentiation
C. H. Waddington, University of Edinburgh

Additional Volumes in Preparation

CURRENT CONCEPTS IN BIOLOGY

A Macmillan Series

NORMAN H. GILES, WALTER KENWORTHY, JOHN G. TORREY, Editors

Algae and Fungi

C. J. Alexopoulos
H. C. Bold
The University of Texas

Macmillan Publishing Co., Inc.
New York
Collier Macmillan Publishers
London

To

J. C. A. and M. D. B.

Library of Congress catalog card number: 67–16708

Macmillan Publishing Co., Inc.
866 Third Avenue, New York, New York 10022

Collier Macmillan Canada, Ltd.

Printed in the United States of America

Printing 10 11 12 13 14 Year 7 8 9

Preface

ALTHOUGH the algae and fungi were grouped together as classes of the division Thallophyta in the late nineteenth century and first three decades of the twentieth, such classification has been abandoned in modern polyphyletic treatments of the plant kingdom. In light of this, one may question the preparation of a text which treats the algae and fungi jointly. In justification it may be stated that, in spite of the dismemberment of the Thallophyta, it is still traditional to teach courses at several levels in which the algae and fungi form the subject matter. Although all algae and fungi may not, in fact, be phylogenetically closely related, these organisms possess many common attributes with respect to organization and reproduction—for example, the filamentous habit, flagellated reproductive cells, and degrees of gamete differentiation ranging from isogamy to oögamy. Furthermore, it is quite possible that, as our knowledge is augmented by biochemical and ultrastructural studies, real evidences of relationships between certain algae and fungi may be uncovered.

Although this text is based on consideration of illustrative types, emphasis has also been placed on presentation of principles and generalizations. The authors have tried very hard to avoid burdensome minutiae, but certain basic data are indispensable to the understanding of principles and generalizations if the reader is to be provided with substance and not mere shadow. Because of the brevity of treatment of the algae and fungi herein, the interested reader has been provided with literature citations of more extend treatments of the organisms involved.

Although one of us (H.C.B.) prepared the material on the algae and the other (C.J.A.) that on fungi, both authors, of course, are responsible for the volume in its totality.

Austin, Texas

C. J. A.
H. C. B.

Contents

CHAPTER

1

Introduction to the Algae

Definition

The term **algae** (singular, **alga**) is applied to a vast array of organisms of approximately 1,800 genera with 21,000 species which are highly diverse with respect to habitat, size, organization, physiology, biochemistry and reproduction. **Phycology** is the study of algae and those who pursue such a study seriously are **phycologists.**

During the latter part of the nineteenth century and the early decades of the twentieth, the term algae was used both as a common name and as a formal taxonomic designation which encompassed these diverse groups. At the present time, however, the differences among these organisms are so strongly emphasized that the formal, collective taxon "Algae" has been abandoned, and a polyphyletic treatment of these organisms prevails. Accordingly, the old class Algae of the Division Thallophyta has been replaced by (usually) eight or nine or more taxa of divisional rank (see pages 26–27). Before considering the current criteria for the classification of algae, let us inquire into the combination of characteristics which distinguishes them from other plants.

What then *are* algae? The answer is not a simple one, inasmuch as habitat, size, organization, physiology and their currently known chemical attributes are inadequate to delimit the algae as a group. The reliable criteria are technical and concern the organization of the sexual stages. In the algae, as distinct from other chlorophyll-bearing plants, three basic alternatives prevail with respect to the sex cells or **gametes.** These are (1) as in the case of unicellular algae, the entire organism may function as a gamete (Figure 1·1A); or (2) the gametes in colonial and multicellular algae may be produced in special *unicellular* containers called **gametangia** (Figure 1·1B); or (3) the gametangia may be *multicellular* each of the component cells being fertile—that is, producing a gamete (Figure 1·1C). The Charophyta (see page 42), which indeed may not be algae, present a possible exception. In most other chlorophyllous plants, in contrast to the algae, sterile cells are associated with the gametes as covering layers (Figure 1·1D).

Occurrence and Habitat

Algae are ubiquitous but are usually overlooked unless they are as obviously abundant as the seaweeds on rocky coasts or floating, often slimy, masses of filaments ("pond scums") or as "water blooms" (Figure 1·2). The last, which are dense populations of suspended microscopic algae, develop under environmental conditions favorable for the organisms comprising the bloom. Water blooms may be composed of one or more types of algae, and characteristic fungi and animals are generally associated with them. Blooms of *Euglena, Anabaena, Polycystis,* miscellaneous diatoms and of certain dinoflagellates (*Gonyaulax* in the "Red Tide") are very common.

Aquatic algae are present in waters of varying salinity ranging from the dilute solutions in certain springs and lakes, through brackish and ocean waters, to saline pools in which the concentration of solutes is so high that crystallization of salts is occurring. *Dunaliella salina* and certain *Pyramimonas* species, for example, have adapted to an ecological niche in such brines.

Aquatic algae may be unattached and suspended as members of the **plankton** in rivers, lakes and oceans, or attached to shells or rocky and muddy bottoms, to other algae or to aquatic angiosperms, ferns or bryophytes. Algae have been found growing at depths as great as 300 feet in clear waters. Certain combinations of species are characteristically present in rapidly coursing streams and cataracts, and in the adjacent areas moistened by spray.

The phenomenon of zonation of algal species is well known and especially striking in coastal areas with rocky shores and a wide range in tidal amplitude, as, for example, in the Bay of Fundy. In such habitats, rock-inhabiting or lithophilic algae exhibit a "preference" or characteristic distribution at the supratidal, intertidal and subtidal levels. Supratidal and intertidal genera are, in general, characterized by thick, hydrophilic colloidal walls, an evident adaptation to intermittent desiccation. Algal zonation, as it is presumed to be related to algal pigmentation, is discussed in a later section (page 25).

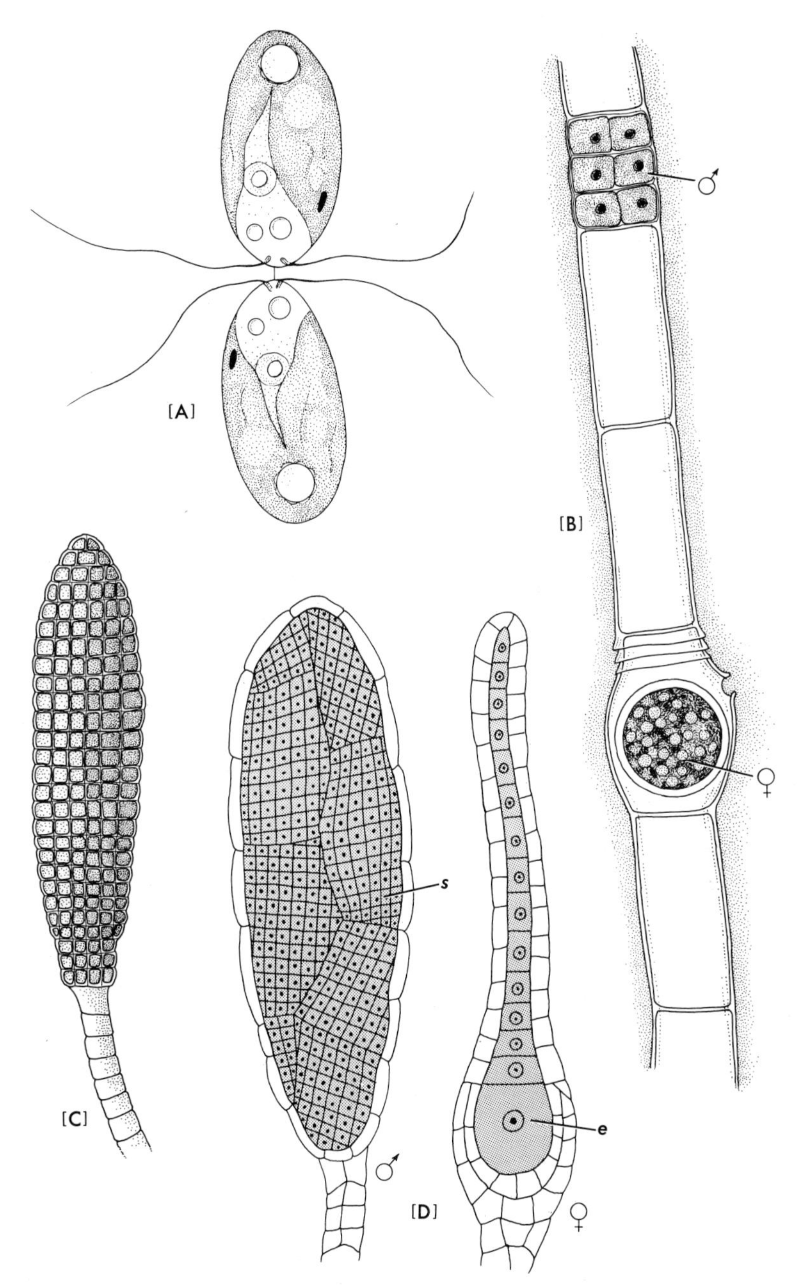

Figure 1·1. Sexual reproduction in algae (A,B,C) and nonalgae (D). A: *Chlamydomonas* sp.—the organisms themselves function as gametes. **B:** *Oedogonium* sp.—gametes are borne in special *unicellular* gametangia (male, above, and female, below). **C:** Multicellular (plurilocular) gametangium of *Ectocarpus,* a brown alga—every cell fertile. **D:** Sex organs of a bryophyte (diagram)—the male organ, antheridium, at the left and the female organ, archegonium, at the right (*s,* spermatogenous tissue; e, egg).

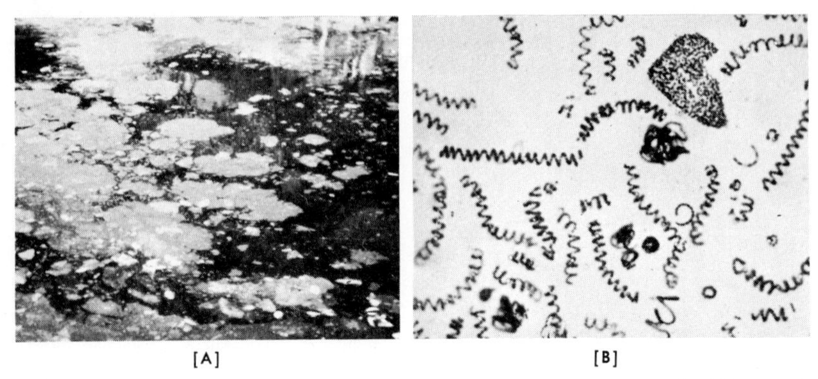

[A] [B]

Figure 1·2. A: Water bloom of *Euglena granulata* in a Texas pond. **B:** Microscopic view of a drop of water from another bloom in which the blue-green algae *Anabaena* (spiral) and *Polycystis* are the dominant organisms.

Although algae in aquatic habitats are familiar to most people, the ubiquity of nonaquatic algae is not as evident. Algae on exposed rocks, buildings, tree bark, mosses, woodwork and soil (including even desert and cave soils) are often mistaken for mosses or lichens. This extra-aquatic algal flora is, as a result, much less well known and appreciated, and the specialized physiological and ecological features of these organisms have not been intensively investigated.

A considerable population of algae is present at the surface and within the subsurface layers of most soils. The number of individuals there is clearly correlated with depth and moisture, algae being more abundant in soils which are moist for long periods and at or near the surface, although they occur abundantly to a depth of one foot. Although the mode of nutrition and the relationships of soil algae with other organisms have not been widely explored, it is clear that certain blue-green algae in the soil, like certain bacteria, can fix gaseous nitrogen. As soil is desiccated, it is carried into the atmosphere and widely distributed as dust; the atmosphere, therefore, at certain times contains a diverse population of airborne algae (and other organisms).

Nitrogen-fixing blue-green algae may be either free-living or endophytic within certain liverworts, aquatic ferns, and the roots of cycads. Some green algae in the soil can utilize organic complexes produced by the degradative activities of bacteria.

Endophytic algae are widespread in protozoa, *Hydra* and sponges and in corals; in the latter relationship, they play a fundamental role in the nutritional balance of the biota of reefs. Certain blue-green and green algae are associated with various types of fungi, the associations forming organisms different from either of the components. These dual organisms comprise the lichens (see page 86).

In contrast to the endophytic algae, a great number of aquatic algae are epiphytic on larger algae or on aquatic angiosperms. There are indications that these associations are not merely fortuitous, but the details remain to be elucidated.

The versatility of algae with reference to solute concentration has been noted above. They are equally wide-ranging with respect to temperature. At one extreme, one may cite the blue-green algae of hot springs in Yellowstone Park, Iceland, and other places; temperatures of about 50–54° C seem to be optimal for their growth. At the other extreme are the various species of the **cryoflora,** the algae of frozen habitats, which occur characteristically on the surface of snows.

A number of parasitic algae have been described. Among these may be cited the green alga *Cephaleuros* which is an intercellular parasite in the leaves of a number of plants, such as *Magnolia, Rhododendron,* tea and pepper. Several genera of parasitic red algae are known. Unfortunately there have been no definitive studies of the nutritional relationships between these parasites and their hosts.

CHAPTER

2

Organization of the Algal Organism

Cellular Organization

Two markedly different patterns of cellular organization occur; these are represented in the terms **prokaryotic** and **eukaryotic.**

The Cyanophycophyta or blue-green algae (often classified with bacteria in the Prokaryota) alone among the algae are prokaryotic in that their nuclear material, deoxyribonucleic acid (DNA), is not delimited from the remainder of the protoplasm by a nuclear membrane (Figure 2·1), but rather it is dispersed to some degree throughout the cell. Correlated with this feature is the absence of membrane-bounded plastids; the photosynthetic lamellae occur freely in the cytoplasm. Also absent are such organelles as the endoplasmic reticulum, mitochondria, and Golgi apparatus. Large aqueous vacuoles, like those which occur in many Chlorophycophyta (for example *Spirogyra*) are absent from the cells of blue-green algae. Furthermore, the cell walls of blue-green algae show some chemical similarity to those of bacteria. Finally, the fact that some blue-green algae may be infected with viruses which resemble bacteriophages emphasizes further the similarity between blue-green algae and bacteria.

By contrast, the cells of eukaryotic algae have their DNA localized within a minutely perforated nuclear membrane (Figure 2·2), their nuclei being essentially similar to those of "higher" plants and animals. Their photosynthetic lamellae are confined within membranes as well-defined chloroplasts. These may be massive, parietal or asteroidal structures, occurring singly within each cell, or they may be ribbon-like, bar-like, net-like or in the form of discrete segments as in nonalgal

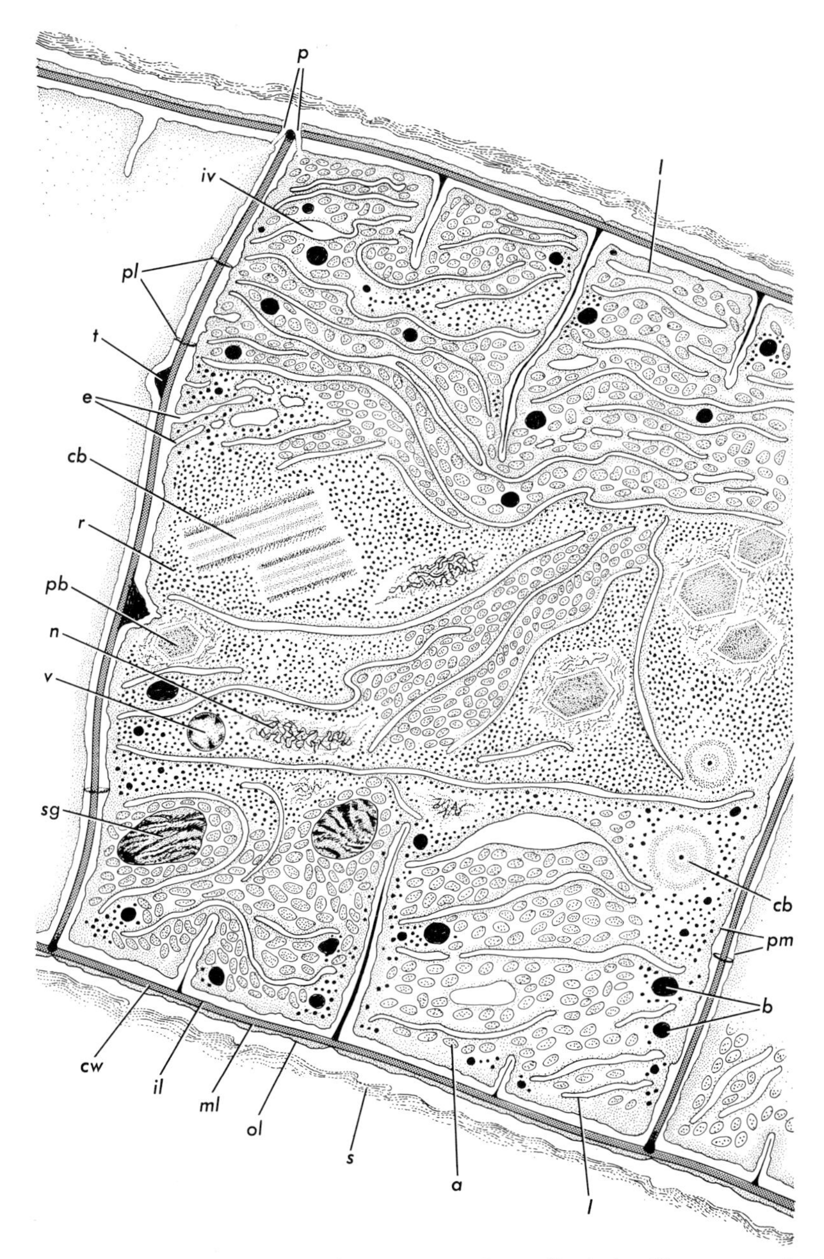

Figure 2·1. Diagram of a median section of a cell of the blue-green alga, *Symploca muscorum*, as seen by electron microscopy. Code: *a*, granules; *b*, granules; *cb*, cylindrical bodies; *cw*, crosswall; e, elaboration of plasma membrane; *il*, *ml*, *ol*, inner, middle, and outer layer, respectively, of inner investment; *iv*, intralamellar vesicle; *l*, lamellae; *n*, nucleoplasm; *p*, pores; *pb*, polyhedral bodies; *pl*, plasmodesms; *pm*, plasma membrane; *r*, ribosomes; *s*, sheath; *sg*, structured granules; *t*, local thickening; *v*, "vacuole-like" inclusions. [From H. S. Pankratz and C. C. Bowen, in *Amer. J. Bot.*, *50*: p. 389, 1963.]

green plants. In many Chlorophycophyta, Euglenophycophyta, Chrysophycophyta, Phaeophycophyta and Rhodophycophyta, specialized regions, the **pyrenoids,** are present within the plastids (Figure 2·2). In the green algae they are usually surrounded by starch grains, in some instances of characteristic form and number, and it is inferred that they are centers for the enzymatic condensation of glucose into starch. It is by no means clear whether or not starch grains are formed elsewhere

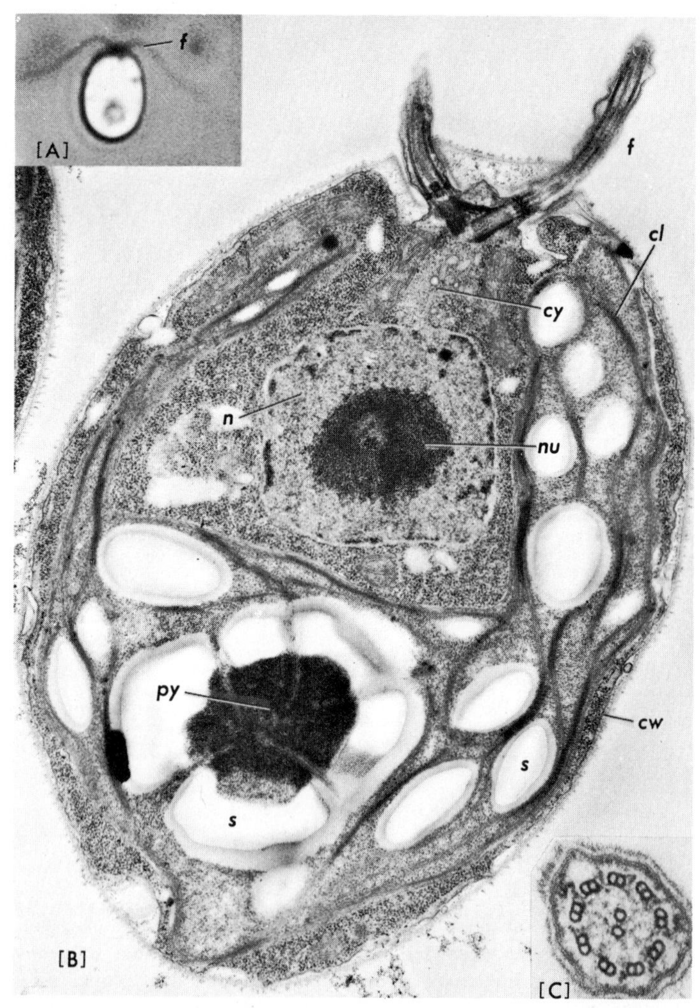

Figure 2·2. The green alga *Chlamydomonas reinhardtii*. A: As photographed in motion with an interference microscope. **B:** As seen by electron microscopy, in median longitudinal section. **C:** Transection of one flagellum. Code: *cl*, chloroplast lamella; *cw*, cell wall; *cy*, cytoplasm; *f*, flagellum; *n*, nucleus; *nu*, nucleolus; *py*, pyrenoid; *s*, starch grain. [Courtesy of Dr. David L. Ringo.]

in the plastids of green algae with pyrenoids; in those algae which lack pyrenoids (for example, *Microspora*) starch does occur. The role of pyrenoids and their relation, if any, to stored metabolites in groups other than the Chlorophycophyta has not been elucidated.

Endoplasmic reticulum, mitochondria and **Golgi bodies** are present in the cells of all eukaryotic algae which have been investigated.

The motile cells of algae (Figures 2·2 and 2·3), like those of fungi, may be flagellate and/or amoeboid. Associated with motility are such structures as contractile vacuoles, flagella, and **stigmata** (singular, **stigma**) ("red eyespots").

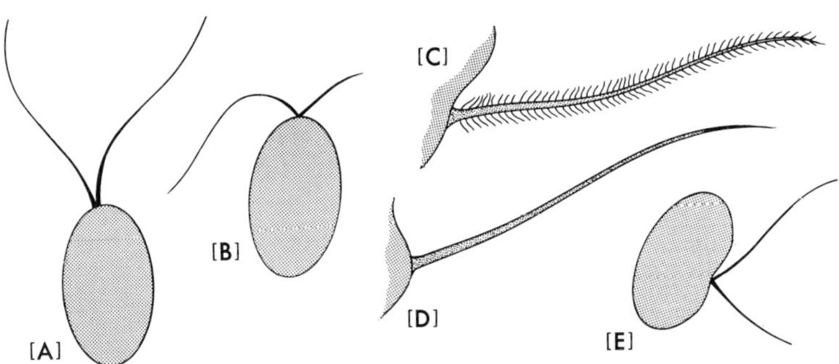

Figure 2·3. Diagrammatic representation of flagellar types among algae. A: Equally biflagellate, apical insertion. **B:** Unequally biflagellate, apical insertion. **C:** A tinsel flagellum. **D:** Flagellum of the whiplash type. **E:** Unequal flagellation, lateral insertion.

Contractile vacuoles range in number from one, two, four to many. They lie near the cell surface, often in close proximity to the flagellar bases. They apparently function in regulating osmotic balance in the cells. Contractile vacuoles are present in both flagellate and amoeboid cells, and in some nonmotile cells as well.

Whatever their number, algal flagella exhibit characteristic organization of being composed of 9 + 2 fibrils (Figure 2·2C) enclosed within a flagellar sheath, the latter continuous with the plasma membrane. The flagella may be equal (isokontan) or unequal (heterokontan) in length (Figure 2·3A,E). Both may be whip-lash (Figure 2·3D) or one may be of the tinsel type (Figure 2·3C). As noted earlier, flagella of algae may be apical or lateral in insertion (Figure 2·3A,B,E).

In many algal motile cells a stigma ("red eyespot") is present (see Figures 6·5A and 6·19A). The stigma may be within the plastid (most Chlorophycophyta and Phaeophycophyta) or not associated with it (Euglenophycophyta). The stigma consists of a number of minute pigment granules. There is evidence both for and against the stigma having a direct role in **phototaxis,** the movement of motile cells in relation to light. It has been demonstrated for some organisms that the action spectrum for phototaxis and the absorption spectrum of the stigma pigment coincide, and that organisms with stigmata orient more rapidly to light than their mutants which lack them. Furthermore, in motile algal colonies the cells in the anterior hemisphere have larger stigmata than those in the posterior, and they may be absent from the most posterior cells. On the other hand, it is also clear that positive phototaxis does occur in motile cells which lack stigmata. It has been hypothesized that the stigma plays an indirect role in phototactic responses, acting as a shading organelle for the true site of light perception, the latter probably associated with the flagella. The pigment in the stigma seems to be a carotenoid.

Knowledge of the chemical composition of algal cell walls has been retarded through lack of adequately sophisticated methods of analysis and, as noted earlier, the available data should be considered as relatively inconclusive. Furthermore, there are difficulties of terminology because of the complications introduced by the presence of a complex of layers at the cell surface, often considered to comprise the cell wall and a sheath or matrix. Where the former ends and where the latter begins is by no means always clear. Furthermore, the distinction between shells or loricas (Figure 6·19E), usually remote from the protoplasm, and cell walls also is at present hardly on a satisfactory basis.

In general, algal cell walls are composed of a variety of carbohydrate materials. These carbohydrates may be either soluble or insoluble in boiling water. The insoluble materials usually are considered as wall materials and the soluble carbohydrates as accessory matrices or sheaths. The latter are outside the cell wall which is (usually) in intimate contact with the plasma membrane. The wall materials are composed of polymers of hexose and pentose sugars and of sugar acids, often a mixture of these.

The major water-insoluble carbohydrates of algal cell walls include cellulose I, mannan, xylan and alginic acid. These compounds have been identified by using extraction and chemical analysis, paper chromatography, electron microscopy and x-ray diffraction.

Cellulose I is widespread among the green algae and occurs also in certain red and brown algae; its presence in blue-green algae has not been confirmed. Mannan occurs in the cell walls of a species of *Porphyra* and in a number of green algae, while water-insoluble xylans have been reported in the walls of certain marine green algae (Siphonales).

Alginic acid, a polymer of D-mannuronic and L-guluronic acids, may comprise up to 25 per cent of the dry weight of some brown algae. The extract of alginic acid in the form of sodium alginate is usually called **algin.**

Water-soluble polysaccharides comprise the amorphous sheaths and matrices of algae (Figures 6·1, 6·2). These include, among others, agar, carrageenin and gelans (xylan) of red algae; pectins and ulvin of the green algae; the fucoidin of brown algae; the mucilaginous compounds of Cyanophycophyta and those of diatoms. The polymers involved are organized from a variety of substances including various hexose and pentose sugars and glycoacids.

Although our knowledge of the chemistry and organization of algal cell walls is being augmented, "an almost inexhaustible field of study remains for the organic chemist and the plant physiologist." [1]

Organization of the Plant Body

There is a wide range of alternative patterns of organization of the plant body, or thallus, among the several algal divisions.

It is almost axiomatic in biology that the simplest organisms are **unicellular**—that is, the organism is composed of but a single cell (Figures 6·1, 6·5). The cells may be motile or nonmotile, spherical or of a variety of other genetically determined shapes, uninucleate, or in relatively few instances, multinucleate.

The cells may have firm walls of cellulose or other material or they may be naked, sometimes with cytoplasmic projections like rhizopodial protozoa (Figure 6·23B).

Traditional speculation has it that failure of separation by the products of cell division gave rise to incipient multicellular aggregates called **colonies,** and that this tendency ultimately became the rule in many organisms. Two types of colony with respect to growth pattern, occur: indeterminate and determinate. Indeterminate colonies consist of aggregates of cells in which cell division is unlimited, so that increasingly large masses result (Figure 6·2). By contrast, in a determinate colony or **coenobium,** the total number of divisions, and accordingly, of component cells, is fixed at the time or origin of the colony and is not augmented later (Figure 6·6A, 6·9A). In either type of colony, the cells may be contiguous or remote from each other. Furthermore, the cells may be arranged irregularly within the colloidal colonial matrix (Figure 6·2B), or in regular geometrical fashion in one or more planes (Figure 6·2A). Finally, colonies may be motile (by means of flagella) like those of *Volvox* (Figure 6·6) or nonmotile like those of *Hydrodictyon* (Figure 6·9A).

The organism consists of a **filament** or chain of cells in many algae.

[1] P. S. O'Colla, Chap. 20, in R. A. Lewin (ed.), *Physiology and Biochemistry of Algae* (see Selected References at end of book).

Filaments (Figures 6·3, 6·10 to 6·12) arise in ontogeny by repeated cell division in a single direction and concomitant coherence of the products of division. Branched filaments (Figure 6·10C) arise by division of certain cells in a new direction. The branches may differ in form or be similar to the main filaments in diameter and pattern of branching. The cells of filaments may be uninucleate or multinucleate.

Foliose or **membranous algae** (Figure 6·14) develop as unbranched filaments in early ontogeny. Division in a direction perpendicular to the first in most cells of the juvenile filament results in two-dimensional expanses. These may be one, two to a number of cells thick, the thicker thalli usually being of firmer texture.

In a number of Phaeophycophyta, Rhodophycophyta (and in the fruiting bodies of many fungi), the growth pattern of the filaments, a more-or-less dense interweaving, has resulted in a pseudoparenchymatous thallus. A tissue composed of thin-walled, living cells, in which contiguous cells have arisen by division of common parent cells is known as **parenchyma.** The *secondary* close association of cells by interweaving of filaments represents a **pseudoparenchyma** (Figure 6·15B,C).

The cells of pseudoparenchymatous algae may be densely packed and firmly coherent, sometimes through establishment of secondary intercellular connections, as in certain red algae; or the association may be loose and the component filaments can be readily separated by pressure. In pseudoparenchymatous organisms there may be a single filament or numerous colorless, central, axial filaments which form the framework or "skeleton" on which the interwoven photosynthetic filaments are supported.

In a large assemblage of marine Chlorophycophyta, the unit of organization is a multicellular vesicle or tube. The latter, usually multinucleate, is interpreted as a multinucleate or coenocytic cell by some and as acellular by others. Two basic patterns of organization occur in this group. In one type, the individual tube or siphon has become increasingly large and branched (Figure 6·15A), while in the second the organism is composed of an intricate system of interwoven tubes and vesicles (Figure 6·15B,C).

Among the plant bodies of algae, several patterns of growth occur. Growth may be generalized—that is, all or almost all of the cells of the thallus continue to divide. This occurs in certain unbranched, filamentous algae and in such a foliose type as *Ulva,* the "sea lettuce." By contrast, growth may be localized usually at the apex or apices or at one or more intervals between base and apex of the plant (intercalary growth). Apical growth occurs in many green, brown and red algae. The apical meristematic zone in some cases is dominated by a prominent apical cell. Intercalary growth occurs, for example, at the junction of the blades and stipes in kelps and in the common green alga *Oedogonium* in which intercalary dividing cells are marked with apical caps (Figure 6·11F).

The vegetative thalli of algae in most instances exhibit as little histological differentiation as those of fungi. Certain brown algae such as the kelps and rockweeds and certain red algae are internally differentiated. The surface layers in these organisms usually consist of one or more layers of cells rich in plastids, which form a photosynthetic cortex, under which occur larger, almost colorless storage cells. In some cases, special hypha-like filaments comprise the central region or medulla. The greatest histological specialization is apparent in certain kelps where highly differentiated, phloem [2]-like sieve cells occur. Although it has not yet been demonstrated that conduction occurs in such cells, translocation does occur in the stipes that contain them.

Finally, with respect to size, there is considerable range in algal organisms. The minute cells of *Chlorella* (Figure 6·7G) and *Chlorella*-like algae may be as small as 2–3 microns [3] in diameter. The cellular nets of the coenobic *Hydrodictyon* (Figure 6·9A) may become 16–18 inches in length, while in many siphonaceous green algae one organism may colonize an area up to 40 feet in length. The largest algae, of course, are some of the giant **kelps** (*Macrocystis* and *Nereocystis*) (Figure 6·29); plants of these genera of more than 150 feet in length have been collected.

---

[2] Xylem (water-conducting cells) and phloem (organic material-conducting cells) comprise vascular tissue in the so-called "higher" plants.

[3] A micron is 0.001 mm.

CHAPTER

3

Methods of Study and Nutrition of Algae

Methods of Study

MACROSCOPICALLY VISIBLE ALGAE or large masses of others may be collected from the field and brought to the laboratory in plastic sacs or collecting jars. The latter, if tightly closed, should not be filled to capacity in order that there be an adequate supply of air; furthermore, collections should be shaded from direct sunlight in hot weather. Coarser marine algae may be collected conveniently in plastic or hard-rubber buckets along with one or two small collecting jars to be used for rare fragments or delicate specimens.

Plankton algae may be collected by towing special plankton nets, composed of fine bolting silk (180 meshes/sq. in.; 50–80 μ pores) through the water. The net becomes clogged with organisms which thus are concentrated for study. Water samples also may be centrifuged to concentrate the plankton algae.

When brought into the laboratory, the collecting jars should be uncovered promptly and illuminated unilaterally. This evokes a concentration of positively phototactic motile forms. Marine specimens are best maintained in running sea water if available.

Soil algae, when conspicuous, may be collected directly from the soil surface. For the many less conspicuous members of the soil algal flora, however, soil samples may be collected in sterile containers and then moistened or submerged in the laboratory with distilled-, rain-water, or any one of a variety of nutrient solutions on culture media. Such treatments usually occasion the development of a rich succession of algal species upon illumination.

Algae may be recovered also from the atmosphere by various sampling methods such as exposing sterile petri dishes with solidified inorganic agar medium for various periods and in various locations. The number of algae in the atmosphere is higher, of course, on windy, dry days when more dust is present.

There is no satisfactory substitute, in most cases, for the study of freshly collected, living algae, since these provide one with an array of taxonomically useful criteria, many of which are not preserved in herbarium specimens. However, the latter are indispensable records of specimens previously identified. Furthermore, it is often not feasible to study freshly collected algae due to remoteness of the field from the laboratory. In such instances, they may be promptly placed in a plant press for drying or preserved in dilute (4 per cent) formaldehyde for future study. Specimens of microscopic algae are often dried on transparent mica strips which are nonbreakable and convenient for later microscopic study.

For many microscopic algae, taxonomic determination is facilitated through maintenance of the organisms in unialgal or axenic culture (see page 16); populations thus become available for continuing comparisons. Furthermore, these living populations may be deposited for continuing maintenance in various culture collections of living algae, among them those at Indiana University in the United States and at Cambridge University in England.

There is no one book or series of books which summarizes all the species of algae currently known to science. The several groups of algae are usually covered in separate, regional floras and/or in monographic treatments of genera or families. Some examples of these are listed in the bibliography. Our knowledge of the world's algal flora is being augmented continually as indicated in the current literature.

Nutrition

The nutritional and environmental requirements of algae, insofar as they are currently understood, have been elucidated largely by studying laboratory cultures growing under controlled conditions. Supplementary and correlated field observations are of prime importance in this connection.

Algal cultures are populations of algae growing under laboratory conditions. Various types or grades of culture have been distinguished including: (1) maintenance cultures; (2) enrichment cultures; (3)

unialgal cultures; (4) axenic or pure cultures; and (5) clonal cultures. These may be defined as follows. **Maintenance cultures** are merely natural collections of algae kept in containers in the laboratory; there they may reproduce and the dominants may be replaced by originally less abundant species in a sort of succession. **Enrichment cultures** also are crude collections or other algal source materials which are treated with specially selected media which favor the rapid increase in the number of one or more desired specific algal species. **Unialgal cultures** are populations in which only a single species of alga is present, although other microorganisms may be associated. An **axenic algal culture** contains a population of a single algal species, all other living organisms being absent. **Clonal cultures** of algae are populations of organisms descended asexually from a single individual. Such cultures may or may not be axenic. For definitive physiological studies, axenic clonal cultures are indispensable.

The algae, broadly speaking, like other chlorophyllous plants, require C, H, O, P, K, N, S, Ca, Fe, and Mg and also traces of Mn, Bo, Zn, Cu, and Co. For certain organisms additional elements are required such as Si for diatoms and Mo for nitrate reduction in *Scenedesmus*. Certain substitutions are possible such as Ru for potassium and Sr for calcium. Nutritive requirements are determined by growing the organisms in a **culture medium** or solution in which known concentrations of these elements, in the form of various compounds, have been dissolved. Although comparatively few (probably less than 0.01 per cent) of the species of algae have been studied in this way, a considerable amount of data has been accumulated on the basis of which certain *tentative* generalizations have been formulated. Most of this information is based on cultural studies of green algae; our knowledge of the nutrition of the other groups is highly fragmentary.

Algae do not differ markedly from other chlorophyllous plants with respect to the major and trace elements required for growth. They are able to use a wide variety of inorganic compounds as sources of the required major and trace elements. The C, H, and O are, of course, usually available in the culture medium since both CO_2 and O_2 are usually present. Inasmuch as the *p*H of the medium may change as certain ions are absorbed by the algae in a culture vessel, the media are usually *buffered* to maintain the *p*H. Phosphates are commonly used inorganic buffers. The phosphate required for algal growth may be supplied as both the monobasic (for example, KH_2PO_4) and dibasic (for example, K_2HPO_4) salt, each of these being used in suitable concentration to provide the desired *p*H over a considerable period. At the alkaline range, an organic buffer ("Tris"-hydroxymethyl aminomethane) has proven especially effective as a long-time buffering agent which itself is apparently not metabolized. Many media have been utilized in growing algae. In general, blue-green and planktonic algae require more dilute media than other algae. Culture media may be solidified by the addition of 1–2 per cent of agar, a relatively inert colloidal extractive of certain red algae (see page 64).

Algae which can grow in an entirely inorganic medium (in the presence of light) like that cited above are said to be **photoautotrophic.** In other words, using light energy, they are able to synthesize their protoplasm from exclusively inorganic sources. Although photoautotrophism may be demonstrated in laboratory cultures, there is some question whether it is the exclusive method of nutrition of any alga in a natural environment. A number of algal species require in addition certain vitamins, usually B-12, thiamine or biotin; such algae are said to be **photoauxotrophic,** this latter term signifying a growth factor requirement—in this case a vitamin.

Cultural studies with various media have shown that some algae are obligately photoautotrophic—that is, they are unable to utilize organic substances of any kind as a substitute for an inorganic source of any of the required elements.

In contrast to photoautotrophic species, a number of algae are **heterotrophic,** either facultatively or obligately so. Heterotrophic organisms do not synthesize their protoplasm solely from inorganic sources but require some of the essential elements, usually carbon and/or nitrogen in the form of energy-rich organic compounds. Several algae in which the photosynthetic mechanism is impaired require an organic carbon source, acetate, for example, for optimal growth. Such organisms are obligately heterotrophic. Some of these can grow anaerobically.

A number of photoautotrophic species can be cultivated in darkness (some retaining their chlorophyll) as long as they are supplied with organic substrates which they can metabolize. Such organisms are facultatively heterotrophic.

Several algae, among them a species of *Ochromonas* (Figure 6·23A) and certain dinoflagellates may digest solid particles of food; such organisms are **phagotrophic.**

With respect to the major elements they require, algae are able to use a wide range of inorganic and organic sources and probably do so in natural habitats. For example, the important element nitrogen may be used by many algae in such alternate forms as nitrate, nitrite, ammonia, urea, certain amino acids, purines, and even as casein and gelatine; the latter proteins may be used through the extracellular enzymatic activity of certain algae.

This brief discussion, admittedly incomplete, indicates that algae are quite versatile in their nutrition and nutritional requrements.

Although in nature, *p*H of the natural body of water seems to be correlated with the distribution of certain species, careful laboratory investigations of range of *p*H tolerance indicates that some species have a wide range; for example, *Eremosphaera viridis,* which occurs abundantly in nature in acid waters, grows well in laboratory culture at *p*H 7.2.

CHAPTER

4

Reproduction in Algae

REPRODUCTION SIGNIFIES, in part, replication or increase in the number of individuals in a population. In plants in general (in contrast to most animals)[1] and especially in algae, increase in numbers may be readily effected by some form of fragmentation of the plant body, naturally-occurring or induced. This is sometimes called **vegetative propagation.**

In noncoenobic colonies, once they have achieved considerable size, lobes separated from the mass may develop into new colonies. This occurs in nature in *Nostoc* (Figure 6·4A,B), *Synura* (Figure 6·24B), and *Dinobryon* (Figure 6·24C) for example. In the blue-green algae, filaments break up into motile[2] segments of varying length called **hormogonia** (Figure 6·3A–C). *Spirogyra* and other filamentous algae also may undergo fragmentation, the segments in all cases having the potentiality of growing into longer filaments.

In unicellular organisms, division of the cell into two or more identical daughter cells, obviously results in increase in the number of individuals.

In a number of algae, special types of cells are produced periodically as agents of replication of the organism. These include, among others, zoospores, aplanospores, hypnospores, autospores and akinetes. In addition, a number of specialized spores will be discussed with the illustrative genera.

Zoospores are flagellate motile cells (Figure 6·10B) produced singly or in groups by the cell or cells of nonmotile organisms. They vary with respect to flagellar number, common numbers being two, four or many.

Aplanospores (Figure 6·7F) of algae are nonmotile spores which are potentially motile (like zoospores) but which, for some reason, omit

[1] There are, of course, exceptions as in the echinoderms, earthworms, flatworms, etc.

[2] The mechanism of the motility is not understood.

the motile phase. Thus, aplanospores are potentially zoospores.[3] Aplanospores which develop thick walls are termed **hypnospores.**

Autospores (Figure 6·7G), in contrast to aplanospores, lack the potentiality for motility; they are nonmotile miniatures of the parent cell which produces them. Finally, **akinetes** (Figure 6·4D) arise by the thickening of the wall layers of ordinary vegetative cells themselves. They may germinate at the conclusion of dormancy directly into new plants of the species or into zoospores.

Now all the methods and agents of reproduction cited above have in common that the reproductive agent (zoospores, aplanospores, hypnospores, etc.) can develop into a new individual *without* union with another cell—that is, they are agents of **asexual reproduction.** Asexual reproduction results in the development and maintenance of a stable population of similar individuals, although, of course, mutations may occur and be transmitted to progeny of the mutant.

By contrast, in most algal groups the reproductive process involves: (1) the union of cells (**plasmogamy**); (2) union of nuclei (**karyogamy**); and (3) mingling of chromosomes bearing certain combinations of genes (**genomes**). Along with these phenomena, an additional one, **meiosis,** follows in all organisms which exhibit the other three. These four phenomena are involved in all **sexual reproduction** in algae; sexual reproduction may, indeed, be defined by these component features. Meiosis, of course, is a type of nuclear division in which the two sets of parental chromosomes with their genes are once again segregated, not necessarily, however, in exactly the same pattern as that in which they were brought together, so that new combinations may arise.

It will be recalled that algae are defined in terms of their arrangements for sexual reproduction (pages 1–2). In unicellular motile organisms, the organisms themselves may serve as gametes or cellular agents of sexual union (Figures 1·1A and 6·5C–F). In nonmotile algae, special flagellate or amoeboid gametes are produced either by the vegetative cells or by specialized cells called **gametangia** (Figures 1·1B and 6·11). When the gametes are so markedly dimorphic that one, the **sperm** or **spermatium** [1] is minute and motile and the other, the **egg,** is larger and nonmotile, the male gametangium is called the **antheridium** or **spermatangium**[1] and the female the **oogonium** or **carpogonium.**[4]

The pronounced dimorphism of the sperm and egg (Figures 6·11, 6·30D,E) which unite is called **oogamy.** Where the gametes, although differing in size are both flagellate or amoeboid, the condition is called **heterogamy.**

---

[3] The usage of this term with respect to fungi, is less restrictive (see page 90).
[4] As in the Rhodophycophyta.

In many algae the uniting gametes are indistinguishable *morphologically* (see below, page 33) a condition designated **isogamy** (Figures 1·1A and 6·5C).

It is often implied or stated that oogamy is an "advanced" form of heterogamy and thus a "higher" level of sexual reproduction. However, it is clear that, whether or not the gametes are dimorphic, the four phenomena which comprise sexual reproduction in algae occur in every case—be it in isogamy, heterogamy or oogamy.

In some species of algae, the compatible gametes arise from one individual or in one **clone**; the latter is a population descended from one individual. In such cases the individual or clone or species, as appropriate, is designated **bisexual.** In other algae, the compatible gametes arise from different individuals or clones which, accordingly, are designated **unisexual.** In bisexual *clones,* individuals may differentiate into males and females; in this case the *individuals* are unisexual. Thus in at least one strain of *Volvox aureus,* a population derived by asexual reproduction of one individual gives rise to both male and female colonies.

Although sexual reproduction was observed in algae at least as early as 1782, and although genetics and cytology have revealed its biological function and role in evolution, namely that of providing new combinations of characters and, accordingly, heterogeneous populations (in contrast to those in asexual reproduction), we are ignorant regarding its origin and largely ignorant of the factors which evoke and control it in algae and many other organisms.

A number of algae are of interest in this connection. In *Protosiphon,* certain species of *Chlorococcum,* and in *Chlamydomonas,* for example, the cells produce biflagellate cells which may function either as zoospores or gametes. In a number of other algae in which the gametes differ morphologically from zoospores (*Ulva, Cladophora,* for example), the gametes may develop without union—that is, **parthenogenetically**—into new individuals. According to the "starvation" theory of the origin of sexuality, the cell union of sexuality is a result of an attraction between nutritionally depleted cells which could not develop further unless such union occurred. It would seem that experimental nutritional studies of the organisms just cited in relation to sexuality would shed further light on the problem of the origin of sexuality.

Of all the algae, the sexual process of *Chlamydomonas* (see page 33) (and here only in 3 or 4 of hundreds of species) has been studied most thoroughly under rigorously controlled conditions. By these studies it has been demonstrated that periodicity of light, optimal temperatures, depletion of nitrogen [5] in the culture medium and abundant CO_2 are important factors in evoking sexuality. These same factors have proven effective in two species of *Oedogonium.*

[5] Except in *C. moewusii.*

Although it was long well known in plants other than algae and in animals that compatible gametes were attracted to each other chemically, very few algae have been investigated in this respect.

In *Chlamydomonas,* the chemical attractant causes a clumping or grouping of compatible gametes through agglutination of the flagellar tips. An extract of flagella of one strain which causes clumping of the opposite strain has been determined to be a glycoprotein. In *Oedogonium cardiacum* capillary tubes with noncellular extracts of mature (oogonium-bearing) female plants and the supernatant from cultures of such plants attract the sperms. In another species of *Oedogonium* with dwarf males (Figure 6·11F), the sexual process has recently been analyzed. The results indicate that probably four different chemical mechanisms regulate the rather complex process. In *Volvox aureus,* the sperm bundles are attracted chemotactically to the female colonies. Furthermore, the male colonies produce a substance which stimulates maturation of immature colonies as males.

Algae in which sexual reproduction occurs exhibit three fundamentally different types of **life cycle.** By this term is signified the process and events which transpire, starting with one individual until a new generation of similar individuals is again produced. The critical points in these life cycles are gametic union (which includes plasmogamy and karyogamy), meiosis, and the interval and nature of the tissue or plant between these events. The three basic types of algal life cycle may be summarized as follows:[6]

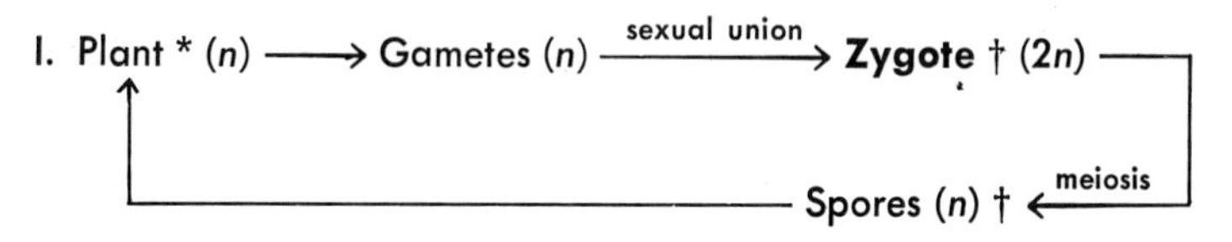

II. **Plant** (2n) —meiosis→ Gametes (n) —sexual union→ **Zygote** (2n)

III. Plant (n) → Gametes (n) —sexual union→ **Zygote** (2n) → **Plant** (2n)
meiosis
Spores ‡(n)

* More than one if unisexual.

† The zygote in most cases forms four or more of haploid entities, each of which has the potentiality of growng into a new plant.

‡ May be zoospores as nonmotile spores (for example, tetraspores, page 59).

[6] Diploid phases are printed in boldface type.

Type-I and type-II life cycles are said to be **haplobiontic** in that only a single form of the plant (biont) occurs in nature. In type-I life cycles, the plant is haploid while in type-II it is diploid. Both haploid and diploid individuals represent the species in type-III or **diplobiontic** life cycles in which occurs an alternation or regular sequence of two *free-living* individual (haploid and diploid) organisms. When the latter are morphologically similar, the alternation is said to be **isomorphic**; in **heteromorphic** alternation, the two sequential organisms differ morphologically.

Several modifications of these three basic types of life cycles occur in algae. In type-III life cycles the diploid plant may reduplicate by producing diploid spores and the haploid plant by parthenogenetic germination of single gametes. In many Rhodophycophyta, the type-III cycle is further modified by the interpolation of a diploid phase, the **carposporophyte** (Figure 6·34C), between the zygote and the free-living diploid tetrasporophyte (see page 59). Furthermore, among Rhodophycophyta, a number of deviations from the type-III life cycle have been noted. These are often associated with marine populations of a species in a particular locality. For example, on the east coast of America, *Rhodymenia* is known only as a diploid plant (tetrasporophyte).

It seems to be generally accepted that the alternants in type-III life cycles are homologous with the gametophytes and sporophytes of land plants. The Chlorophycophyta is the only division of algae in which all three types of life cycle occur. Types II and III characterize the Phaeophycophyta and types I and III the Rhodophycophyta, of the major groups of algae.

CHAPTER

5

Classification of Algae

THE CLASSIFICATION of algae has continually been modified since its "official" beginning in the 1753 edition of Linnaeus' *Species Plantarum.* Then the algae were included in the class Cryptogamia along with other organisms which we now recognize to be mosses, vascular cryptogams ("Pteridophytes") and fungi. In natural or phylogenetic systems [1] of classification, alterations in the classification of algae (and other plants) are made as a result of augmentation of our knowledge with concomitant revision of putative relationship. This has resulted in the present, largely polyphyletic [2] system in which the algae are grouped in seven to eleven categories of divisional rank. The divisions and the criteria on which their circumscription is based are summarized in Table 5·1. Pigments, reserve metabolites ("stored food") and flagellation have proven to be the most reliable general criteria. The nature of the cell walls often given in similar tables, but here omitted,[3] should be regarded as subject to revision following more extensive and more sophisticated chemical and physical appraisal. Furthermore, our knowledge of the comparative chemistry of the several pigments and storage products is so fragmentary, especially in relation to the genetics and evolution of the organisms, that it is quite possible our current polyphyletic groupings may be modified into a more monophyletic system in the future.

Certain conclusions may be drawn from the data in Table 5·1, as follows: All the divisions of algae contain chlorophyll *a.* Associated

[1] These purport to represent real, evolutionary relationships.
[2] Having many distinct lines of evolutionary history.
[3] See, however, statements regarding algal cell walls on pages 10, 11.

with chlorophyll *a* in the several divisions are special combinations of accessory pigments, including other chlorophylls, carotenoid pigments (carotenes and xanthophylls) and phycobilin pigments. Inasmuch as the absorption spectra of the accessory pigments have peaks at wavelengths other than those of chlorophyll *a,* the role of these pigments seems to be, at least in part, one of trapping supplementary light energy which may be transferred and used by chlorophyll *a.* A more intimate connection with the photosynthetic process has been suggested for certain of the accessory pigments.

The chemical structure of the chlorophyll *a* molecule is well known; chlorophylls *b, c, d* and *e,* insofar as their structure is known, differ only in minor features. Carotenoid pigments include oxygen-free, long-chain, unsaturated hydrocarbons, the **carotenes,** and the **xanthophylls** which are oxygenated derivatives of the carotenoids. β-carotene is the most widely distributed carotene, while fucoxanthin and zeaxanthin are examples of widely distributed xanthophylls. Phycobilins are red and blue pigments linked to proteins. Phycocyanin, allophycocyanin and phycoerythrin are examples of phycobilins.

It seems probable (but it has not been unequivocally demonstrated for all) that these three classes of photosynthetic pigments are associated with the sacs or lamellae of the algal cell, whether these lamellae are or are not (blue-green algae) confined within chloroplasts.

A relationship between the stratification of algae and their pigmentation has sometimes been postulated. According to this hypothesis, either the intensity of the light or its quality (wavelength), or both, determine zonation. Inasmuch as the phycoerythrin of red algae adapts them to absorption of blue and violet light, one would expect these to grow at greater depths, where this wavelength of light prevails, whereas in shallower waters one would expect a predominance of green algae which would use light of longer (red) wavelengths in photosynthesis. The brown algae would be expected to be intermediate. While examples of this type of zonation have been observed, it is common to find members of all three groups of algae at a given depth level. For instance, a recent study of zonation on the south coast of Malta indicated that there was not a clear-cut zonation of green, brown and red algae with depth. The Phaeophycophyta were dominant nearest the surface; the Chlorophycophyta became increasingly dominant between 15 and 60 meters; the Rhodophycophyta were present between 15 and 60 meters, in most significant amounts between 30 and 45 meters.

A final point about the phycobilin pigments is of interest. It has been demonstrated experimentally that change in the wavelength of incident light may evoke a reversible color change in certain organisms. For example, a species of the blue-green alga *Oscillatoria* became blue in green light, yellow in blue-green, blue in yellow and green in red light.

TABLE 5·1

Some Noteworthy Attributes of the Algal Divisions [a]

DIVISION	PIGMENTS [b]	STORAGE PRODUCTS	FLAGELLATION
Cyanophycophyta	Chlorophyll *a* β-carotene Antheraxanthin Aphanicin Aphanizophyll Flavacin Lutein Myxoxanthin Myxoxanthophyll Oscilloxanthin Zeaxanthin Allophycocyanin Phycocyanin Phycoerythrin	Cyanophycean starch (probably amylopectin portion of starch), proteins	Absent
Chlorophycophyta	Chlorophylls *a* and *b* α-[c] and β-carotene Astaxanthin Lutein Neoxanthin Siphonein [d] Siphonoxanthin [d] Violaxanthin Zeaxanthin	Starch, oils	1,2,4 to many, equal apical or subapical insertion
Charophyta [e]	Chlorophylls *a* and *b* β-carotene γ-carotene Lycopene	Starch	2, subapical, equal (on sperms)
Euglenophycophyta	Chlorophylls *a* and *b* β-carotene Antheraxanthin Astaxanthin Lutein Neoxanthin	Paramylon, oil	1,2, or 3 equal, slightly subapical
Xanthophycophyta	Chlorophyll *a* β-carotene Lutein Neoxanthin	Chrysolaminarin, oils	2, unequal, apical

TABLE 5·1 (Cont'd)

Some Noteworthy Attributes of the Algal Divisions [a]

DIVISION	PIGMENTS [b]	STORAGE PRODUCTS	FLAGELLATION
Chrysophycophyta	Chlorophyll *a* and c [d] β-carotene Lutein Diadinoxanthin Diatoxanthin Dinoxanthin Fucoxanthin	Chrysolaminarin, oils	1,2, (equal or unequal) apical
Baccilariophycophyta	Chlorophylls *a* and c β-carotene ϵ-carotene Fucoxanthin Diatoxanthin Diadinoxanthin	Chrysolaminarin, oils	1 (male gametes), apical
Phaeophycophyta	Chlorophylls *a* and c α- and β-carotenes Diatoxanthin Flavoxanthin Fucoxanthin Lutein Violaxanthin	Laminarin, mannitol, oils	2, lateral
Pyrrophycophyta	Chlorophylls *a* and c β-carotene Diadinoxanthin Dinoxanthin Peridinin	Starch, oils	2, lateral; 1 trailing, 1 girdling
Cryptophycophyta	Chlorophylls *a* and c α- and ϵ-carotene Zeaxanthin Phycocyanin Phycoerythrin	Starch, oils	2, lateral
Rhodophycophyta	Chlorophylls *a* and *d* [c] α- and β-carotenes Lutein Taraxanthin Allophycocyanin Phycocyanin Phycoerythrin	Floridean starch; oils	Absent

[a] For wall attributes see pages 10, 11.
[b] Compiled from various sources, including Bogorad, L. and Nakayama, T. O. M., in Lewin, R. A. (ed.) *Physiology and Biochemistry of Algae*.
[c] In some genera. [d] In Siphonales.
[e] Divisional name indicates doubtful affinity to other algae.

These changes were results of modifications in relative concentration of the cellular pigments. Color changes in relation to incident light are known as **"chromatic adaptation."**

Table 5·1 also indicates that a variety of polysaccharides may be stored by algae, many of them polymers of glucose molecules with variation in the linkage patterns. Oils and cyclic alcohols also occur.

Flagella may be entirely absent, or, when present, differ in number (1 to many—around 120), insertion (apical or lateral), length (equal or unequal) and organization (whiplash or tinsel type) (Figure 2·3).

At the ordinal, familial, and generic levels, phycologists have been notably inconsistent in their treatment of differential criteria. A few examples of such inconsistencies will suffice to illustrate this: (1) In the Chlorophycophyta and Phaeophycophyta, the *orders* are delimited largely on vegetative or somatic characters, variation in reproduction being treated as of secondary importance. In the *division* Rhodophycophyta, in contrast, the orders are at present delimited on the basis of the organization of the female reproductive branch, vegetative attributes being secondary. (2) Among the Chrysophycophyta, the *families* of certain orders are segregated on the basic of flagellar number, while the same criterion is used at the *generic* level in the unicellular motile Chlorophycophyta. These examples merely emphasize that current classifications are, at best, approximations of relationship. As our knowledge of the algae is augmented, classifications will of certainty be revised.

Like all plants, the algae are classified in accordance with the recommendations and prescriptions of the International Code of Botanical Nomenclature.[4] This code recognizes the individual organism as belonging to a species, the species to a genus, the genus to a family, the family to an order, the order to a class and the class to a division. Space does not permit a complete presentation of the categories in classification of the algae.

[4] *Regnum Vegetabile,* Volume 23. Utrecht, 1961.

CHAPTER

6

Illustrative Algal Organisms

Cyanophycophyta (Blue-Green Algae)

APPROXIMATELY 125 GENERA and 1,200 species of freshwater, marine, and terrestrial algae are classified as blue-green algae. Unicellular colonial and filamentous organisms are represented. The distinguishing attributes have, in part, been summarized in Table 5·1 (pages 26, 27) as has the unusual cellular organization of blue-green algae (page 6), this combination of attributes, of course, distinguishes the Cyanophycophyta sharply from all other groups of algae.

UNICELLULAR TYPES

Chroococcus and *Gloeocapsa* [1] (Figure 6·1) are widespread unicellular blue-green algae. The former is usually aquatic, while the latter is often present on moist, shaded rocks or greenhouse flower pots. The cells are surrounded by colloidal sheaths in addition to the cell wall, the latter contiguous with the protoplasm. Cell division or binary fission is the means of multiplication in these organisms. Several generations of cells may cohere after cell division so that incipient colonies are formed.

COLONIAL TYPES

The colonies of blue-green algae may either be flat or more or less spherical, in the latter case, with cells only at the surface or distributed

[1] Often included together in the genus *Anacystis*.

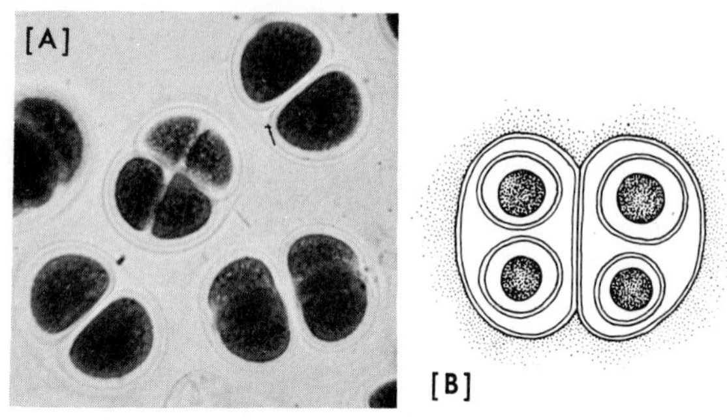

Figure 6·1. Unicellular blue-green algae. A: *Chroococcus turgidus*—note dividing cells and sheaths. **B:** *Gloeocapsa* sp.

throughout the colonial sheath or matrix. The colonies increase in size by division of the component cells and may reproduce by fragmentation.

Merismopedia [2] (Figure 6·2A) is an example of the planar type of colony. The more ubiquitous *Polycystis aeruginosa* [3] (Figure 6·2B) often forms water blooms in late summer and early fall in quiet waters. Its cells are filled with minute, granule-like, gas vacuoles.

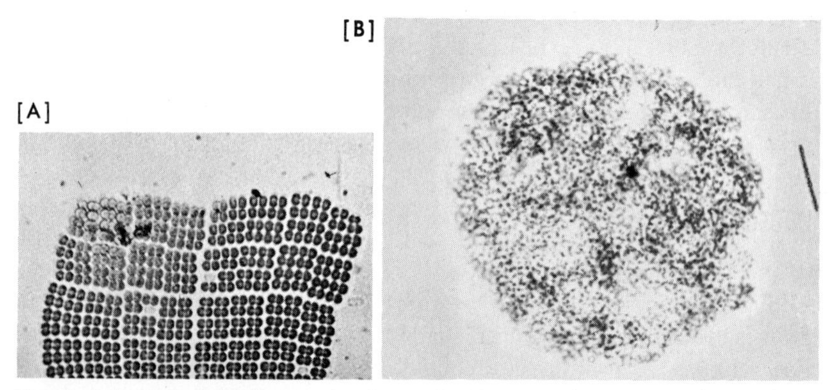

Figure 6·2. Colonial blue-green algae. A: *Merismopedia* sp. **B:** *Polycystis aeruginosa.*

FILAMENTOUS TYPES

Four widespread representatives of the filamentous blue-green algae are illustrated in Figures 6·3 and 6·4. Growth in all is generalized—that is, all the cells are capable of division. All undergo fragmentation to form short chains of cells, called hormogonia. These are motile and grow into new filaments.

[2] Sometimes included in the genus *Agmenellum.*
[3] Sometimes included in the genus *Anacystis.*

Oscillatoria (Figure 6·3A–C) often forms amorphous coatings or floating masses in quiet waters. The masses are structureless and disintegrate when disturbed. The individual filaments [4] are undifferentiated, except for the apical cell, and lack slimy sheaths. The filaments of *Oscillatoria*, as the name implies, exhibit a swaying motion. They also can move backward and forward. Flagella and cilia are absent, and the mechanism for movement in blue-green algae is not understood.

Lyngbya (Figure 6·3D) is very similar to *Oscillatoria* but its cells secrete a firm and prominent sheath.

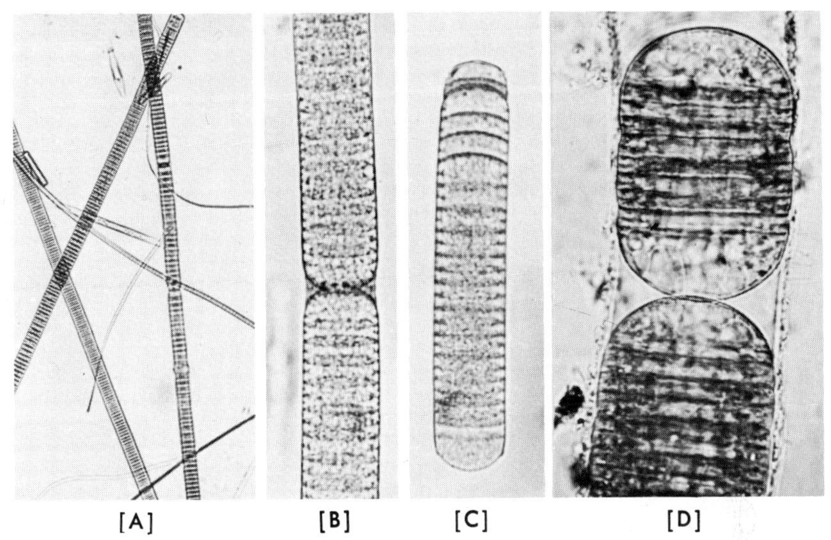

Figure 6·3. Filamentous blue-green algae. A–C: *Oscillatoria*. **A:** Trichomes of two species under low magnification. **B:** Portion of single trichome enlarged—note dead cell and incipient hormogonium formation. **C:** Single hormogonium. **D:** *Lyngbya*—note sheath and hormogonium formation.

In *Nostoc* (Figure 6·4A,B) and *Anabaena* (Figure 6·4C,D), two kinds of specialized cells may develop from the ordinary vegetative or somatic cells, namely, **heterocysts** and **akinetes.** At maturity, heterocysts are transparent (but not empty) cells with thickened walls, the latter usually with polar nodules. Akinetes are also thick-walled cells but with densely granular contents. They can withstand desiccation and germinate into new filaments when moistened.

Chlorophycophyta (Green Algae)

Approximately 425 genera and 6,500 species are included in the green algae. Their most striking common features have been summarized in

[4] Usually called **trichomes** by students of blue-green algae.

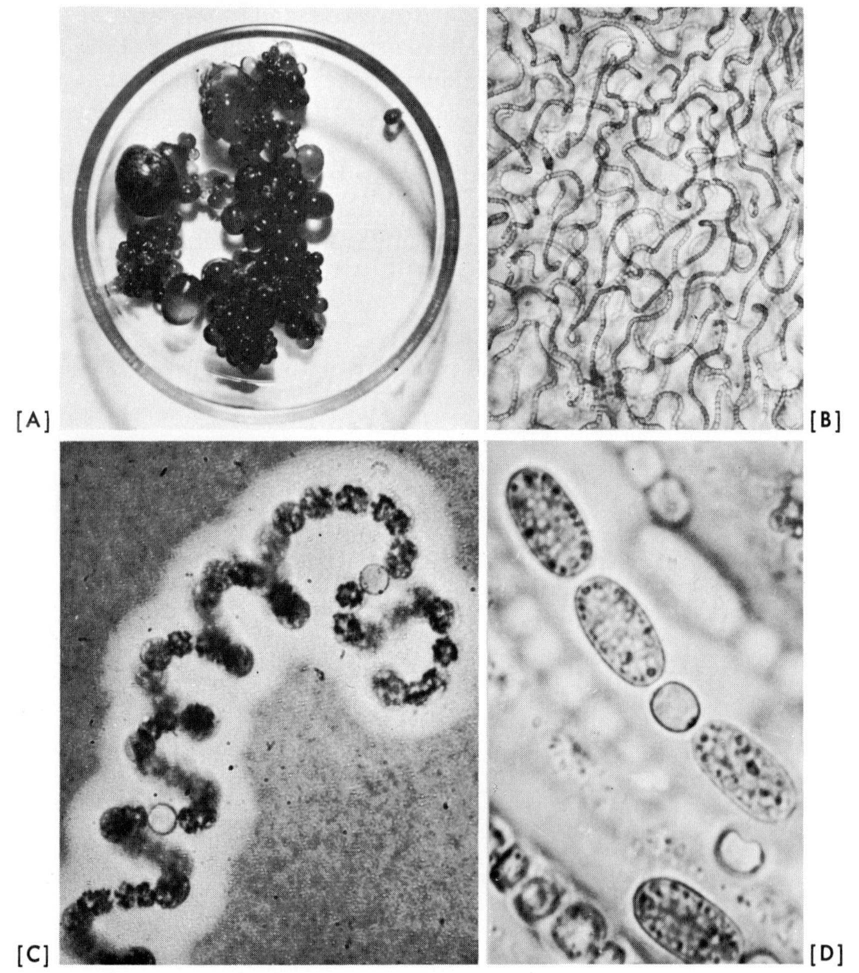

Figure 6·4. A: *Nostoc microscopicum*—freshly collected colonies in a petri dish. **B:** Portion of a colony under low magnification. **C:** *Anabaena* sp.—single trichome with prominent sheath (note two heterocysts). **D:** Four akinetes of *Anabaena*, two connected by a heterocyst.

Table 5·1 (page 26). The green algae are more diverse in organization than the blue-green algae. They include both motile and nonmotile organisms. Selected illustrative types are described briefly in the next few pages.

MOTILE TYPES

Chlamydomonas and *Volvox* are two of numerous genera of motile green algae, the former unicellular and the latter colonial.

Chlamydomonas is a large genus with species widely distributed in soil and fresh water. The organization of the cell is illustrated in Figures 2·2 and 6·5A and described in their legends. Of special interest is the stigma or red eyespot, an aggregate of pigmented granules within the chloroplast which are apparently sensitive to light. The pyrenoid is a prominent, denser region of the chloroplast; starch grains condense on its surface. The cells are motile by means of two flagella which are thrust back stiffly from a parallel forward position which they again assume through a relaxed return to that position so that the cells are "swimming the breast stroke."

In asexual reproduction (Figure 6·5B) the cells become nonmotile and give rise to two to eight small individuals which upon liberation from the parent wall grow until they achieve their genetically determined maximum size.

Under special conditions sexual reproduction occurs (Figure 6·5C–F). In various species of *Chlamydomonas* this may be isogamous, heterogamous or oogamous. The life cycle is type I (page 22).

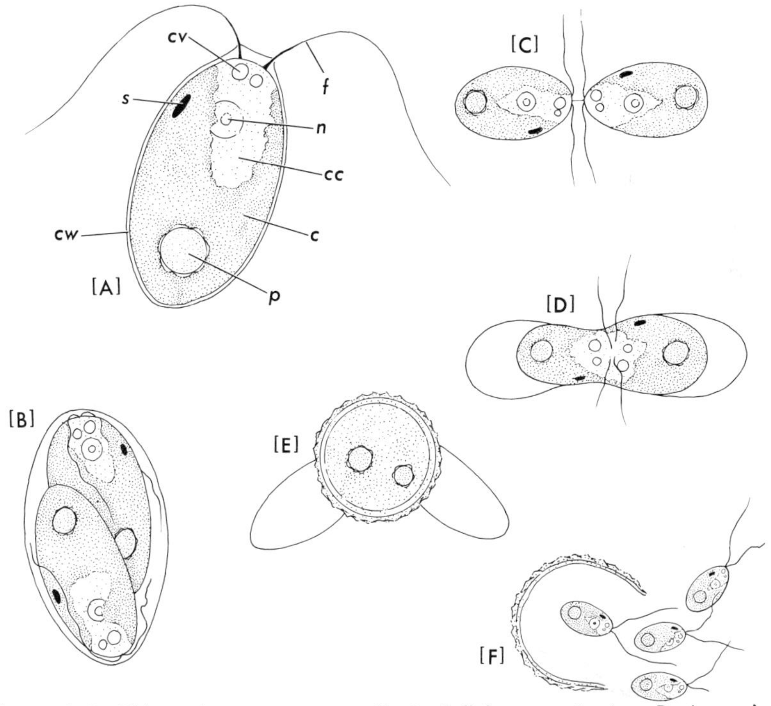

Figure 6·5. *Chlamydomonas moewusii*. A: Cellular organization. **B:** Asexual reproduction. **C–F:** Stages in sexual reproduction—note gamete pair at **C,** union of the gametes at **D,** mature zygote with gamete walls at **E,** and zygote germination at **F.** Code: *c*, chloroplast; *cc*, colorless cytoplasm; *cv*, contractile vacuole; *cw*, cell wall; *f*, flagellum; *n*, nucleus; *p*, pyrenoid; *s*, stigma or red eyespot.

The motile, rolling, coenobic colonies of *Volvox* (Figure 6·6), which may form water blooms, are visible to the unaided eye and have been known for more than three hundred years. The colonies contain from several hundred to thousands of cells arranged at the surface of a watery colloidal matrix. The individual cells are biflagellate and have eyespots and two flagella like those of *Chlamydomonas*.

In asexual reproduction, certain cells at the posterior of the colony divide to form miniature colonies (Figure 6·6A) which are released from the parent; the latter dies when these have all been released.

Sexual reproduction in *Volvox* is oogamous (Figure 6·6B) and the life cycle is type I (page 22).

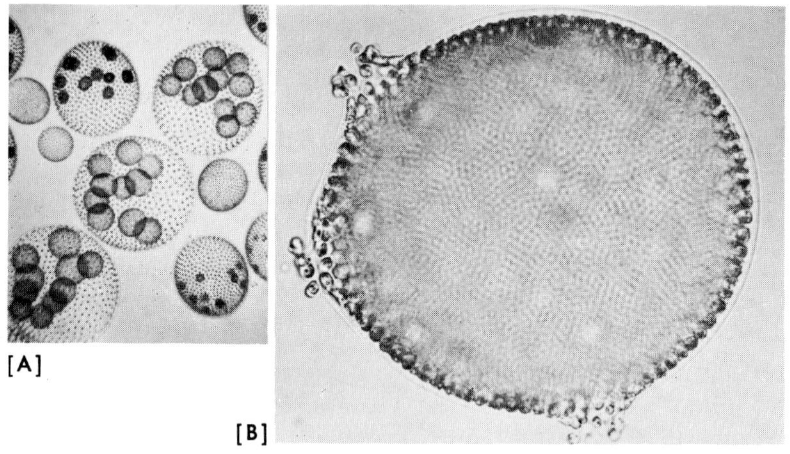

Figure 6·6. *Volvox aureus*. A: Colonies of various ages containing daughter colonies in various stages of development. **B:** Female colony with three groups of sperms penetrating; the light spots are eggs. [**B** courtesy of Dr. William Darden.]

NONMOTILE TYPES

The nonmotile green algae are unicellular, colonial, filamentous, membranous or tubular. They may produce motile zoospores or entirely lack motile stages.

UNICELLULAR TYPES. *Chlorococcum* (Figure 6·7A–F), *Chlorella* (Figure 6·7G,H) and *Eremosphaera* (Figure 6·8) are unicellular nonmotile algae. *Chlorococcum* produces zoospores and may also exhibit sexual reproduction.

Chlorella and *Eremosphaera* reproduce only by forming nonmotile daughter cells. *Chlorella* has become a classical organism through its widespread use in studies of photosynthesis.

COLONIAL TYPES. The water-net, *Hydrodictyon* (Figure 6·9A), a coenobium, is cylindrical; the walls of the cylinder are composed of

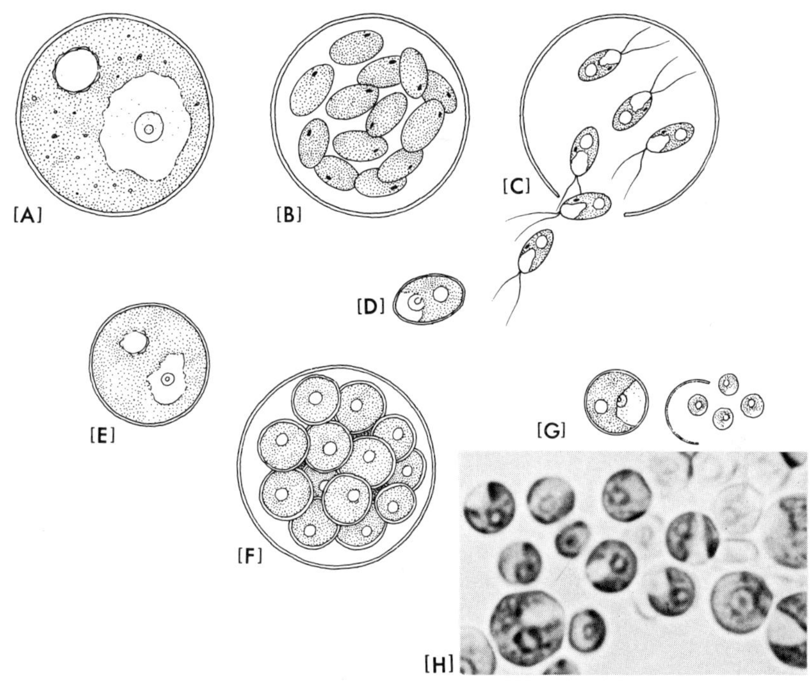

Figure 6·7. A–E: *Chlorococcum* sp. **A:** Vegetative cell. **B:** Zoospore formation. **C:** Zoospore liberation. **D,E:** Stages in development of zoospores into vegetative cells. **F:** Aplanospore formation. **G:** *Chlorella*—one vegetative cell and autospore formation. **H:** *Chlorella*—photomicrograph of living cells. [**H** courtesy of Dr. Melvin Calvin.]

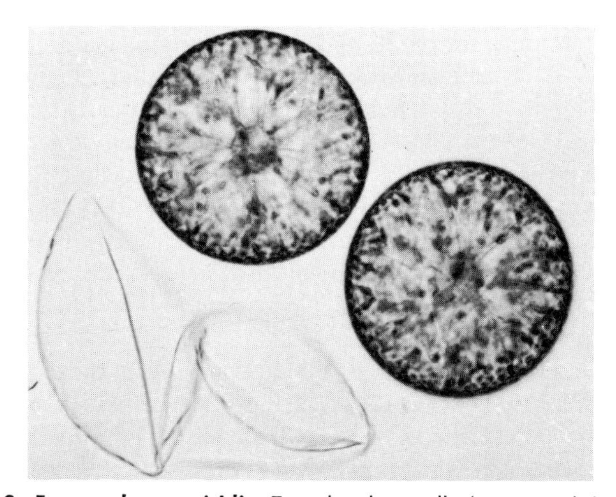

Figure 6·8. *Eremosphaera viridis*. Two daughter cells (autospores) just liberated from mother cell wall—note central nucleus in each cell. [Courtesy Dr. Richard L. Smith.]

cylindrical multinucleate cells arranged in mesh-like groups of 5–8 members, 6 being typical. In asexual reproduction, each individual cell forms hundreds of zoospores which arrange themselves as miniature nets within the parent cell which serves as a mold.

Scenedesmus (Figure 6·9B), a colony composed of four or eight laterally united cells, reproduces asexually by forming nonmotile daughter colonies singly within each parental cell. Some strains of *Scenedesmus* form motile gametes.

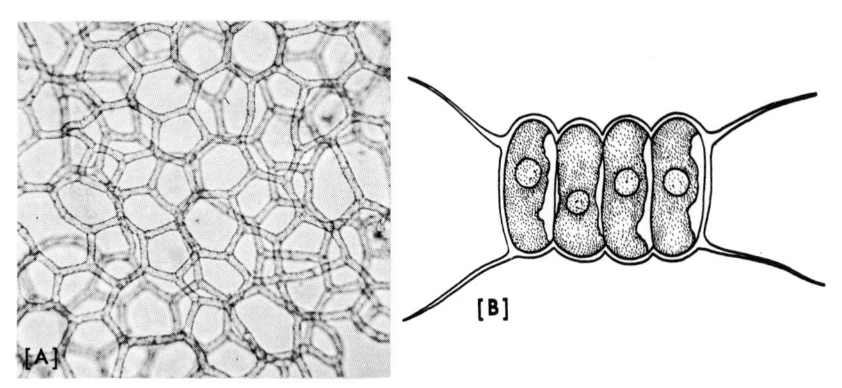

Figure 6·9. A: *Hydrodictyon reticulatum,* the water net—portion of young net under low magnification. **B:** *Scenedesmus quadricauda,* single coenobium.

Filamentous Types. *Ulothrix* (Figure 6·10A,B), *Stigeoclonium* (Figure 6·10C), *Oedogonium* (Figure 6·11), and *Spirogyra* (Figure 6·12) exemplify variations in the filamentous-type of green alga. The first three reproduce asexually by zoospores; the plants are usually attached to rocks or aquatic vegetation by unicellular (Figure 6·10A) or disclike (Figure 6·10C) **holdfasts** at least in their early development.

Ulothrix and *Oedogonium* are unbranched, while *Stigeoclonium* is branched. The zoospores of *Ulothrix* are quadriflagellate and those of *Stigeoclonium* are bi- or quadriflagellate; those of *Oedogonium* have a ring of as many as 120 flagella.

Sexual reproduction is isogamous in *Ulothrix* and *Stigeoclonium* and oogamous (Figure 6·11) in *Oedogonium*. The life cycles in all three are probably type I (page 22).

Spirogyra differs from other filamentous green algae in lacking zoospores and especially in its sexual reproduction which involves the union of amoeboid gametes one of which (considered to be functionally male) passes across a conjugation tube to the other with which it unites to form a zygote (Figure 6·12D–E). The life cycle of *Spirogyra,* as far as known, seem to be type I (page 22).

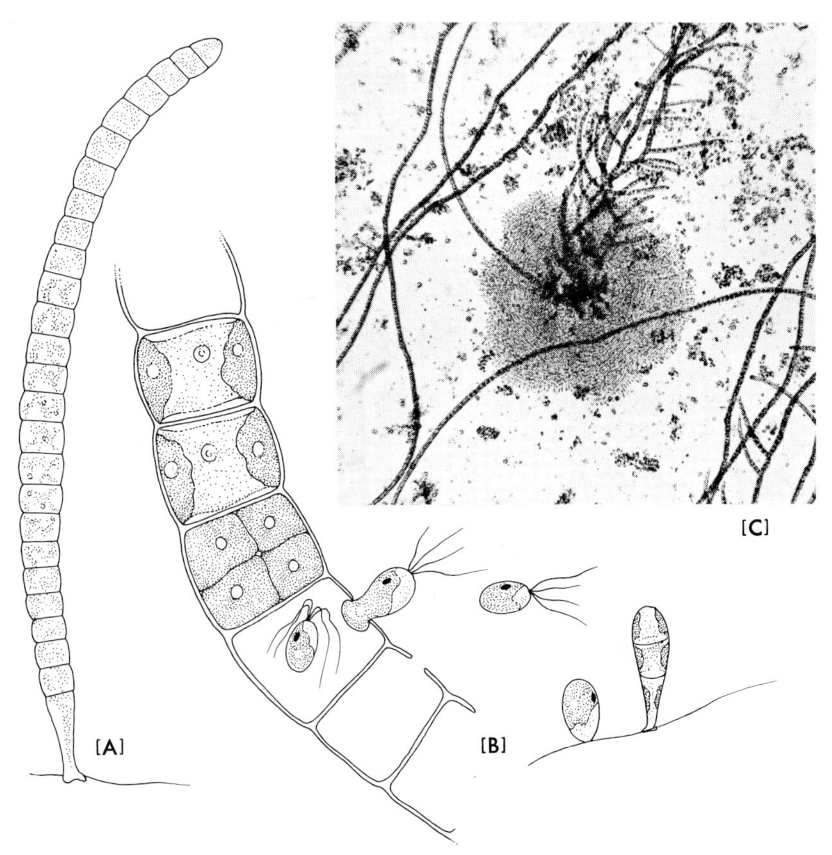

Figure 6·10. A,B: *Ulothrix zonata.* **A:** Single filament attached to substrate by holdfast cell. **B:** Zoospore formation, liberation, attachment, and germination. **C:** *Stigeoclonium* sp. [Courtesy Dr. Elenor Cox].

Mention should be made at this point of a group of unicellular and filamentous green algae, the **desmids** (Figure 6·13). Their cells are composed of mirror-image semicells and their reproduction, like that of *Spirogyra* involves the conjugation of amoeboid gametes.

Membranous Green Algae. *Ulva* (Figure 6·14), the widely distributed marine sea lettuce, is one of several related genera in this group. The blades of *Ulva* are two cells thick. The life cycle is type III (page 22) and both zoospore- and gamete-producing plants are known for most species.

Tubular Organisms. In a large assemblage of (mostly) marine green algae, the unit of organization is a centrally vacuolate tube or siphon. The vacuole is surrounded by a thin layer of protoplasm

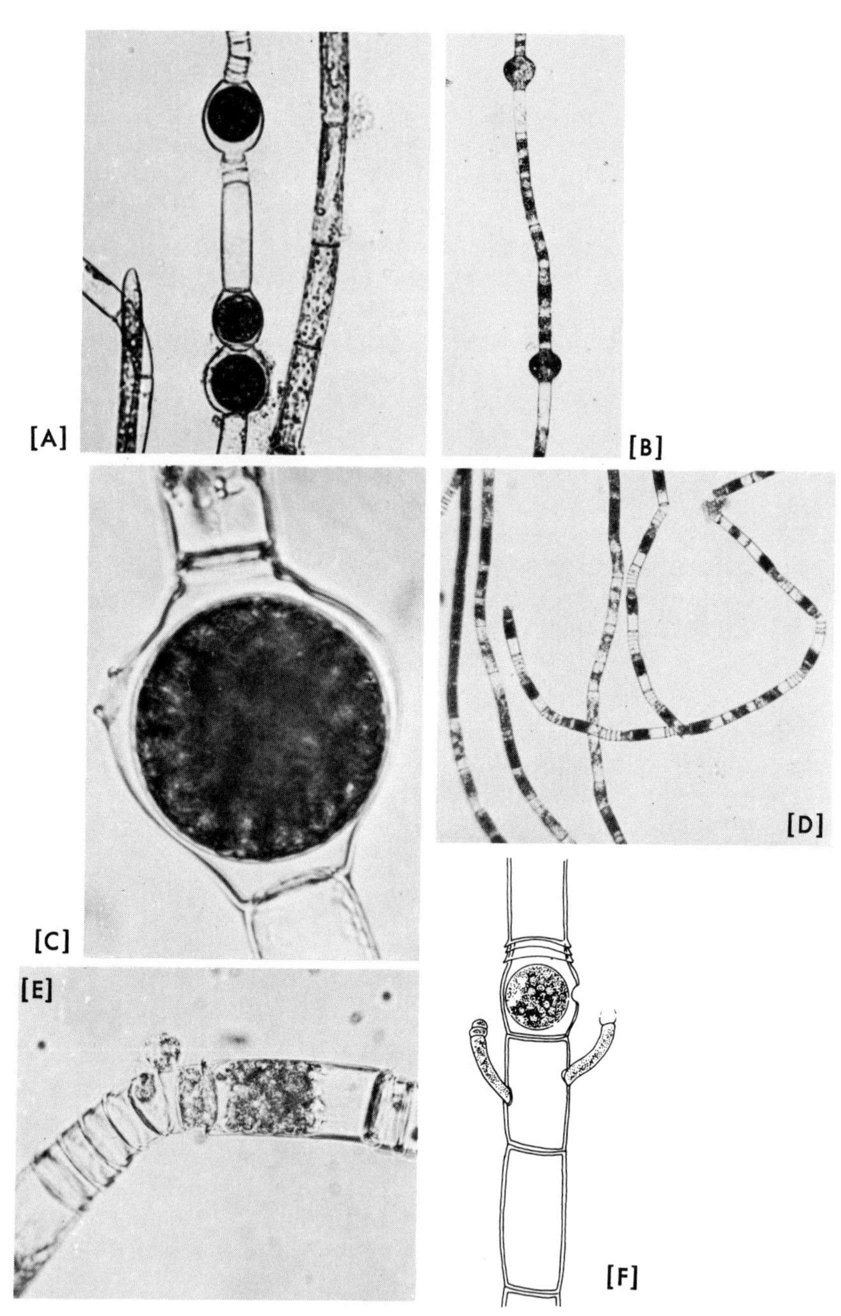

Figure 6·11. *Oedogonium*. **A:** *O. foveolatum,* antheridia and oogonia on the same individual. **B–E:** *O. cardiacum,* species with unisexual individuals. **B:** Female filament with oogonia. **C:** Single oogonium (enlarged) containing young zygote—note pore through which sperm entered. **D:** Male filaments with antheridia. **E:** Sperms emerging from antheridium—note several empty antheridia and immature antheridium, right. **F:** *Oedogonium* sp., a species with dwarf males attached on the cell below oogonium.

containing numerous nuclei and minute plastids. The tubes may be flattened and branching (Figure 6·15A) or interwoven to form complex plant bodies (Figure 6·15B,C). One of the most interesting radially symmetrical forms related to this group is the Mermaid's wine goblet, *Acetabularia* (Figure 6·16). The life cycle of all the tubular and related forms seems to be type II (page 22).

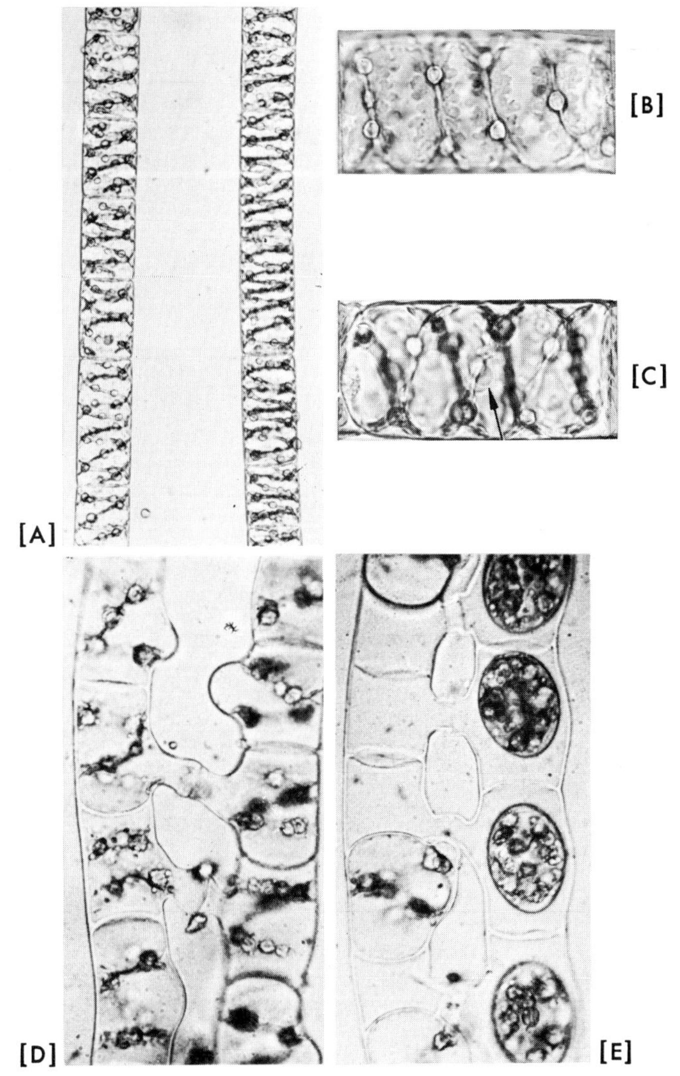

Figure 6·12. ***Spirogyra.*** **A:** Two vegetative filaments. **B:** Single cell in surface view. **C:** The same cell in optical section—note the nucleus (arrow). **D,E:** Stages in sexual reproduction (conjugation)—note conjugation tubes and maturing zygotes (in **E**).

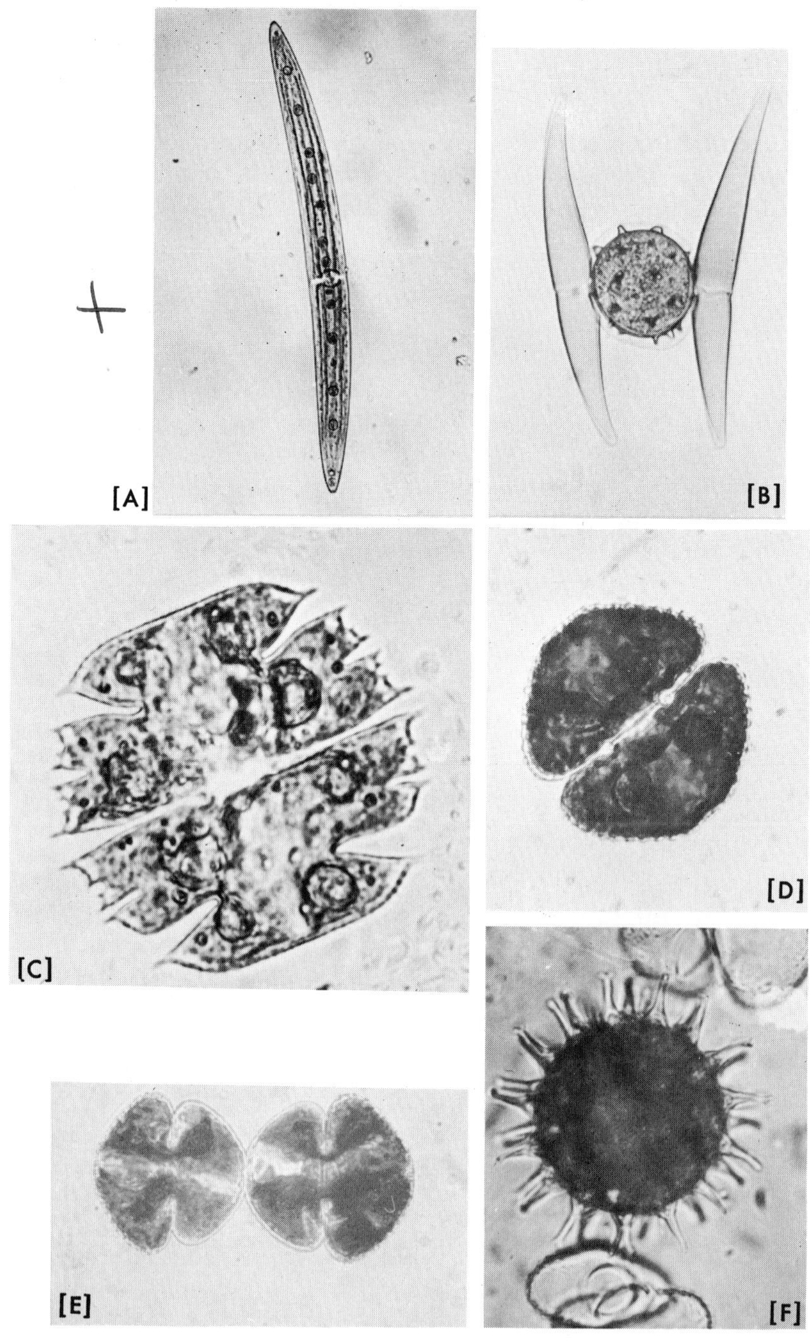

Figure 6·13. Desmids. A: *Closterium* sp. **B:** Sexual reproduction in *Closterium*—note spiny zygote between two empty cell walls. **C:** *Micrasterias* sp. **D–F:** *Cosmarium* sp. **D:** Single vegetative cell. **E:** Dividing cell. **F:** Sexual reproduction—note spiny-walled zygote and empty gamete walls. [**B** from P. W. Cook, in *Phycologia*, 3: p. 11, 1963.]

Figure 6·14. *Ulva lactuca*, sea lettuce.

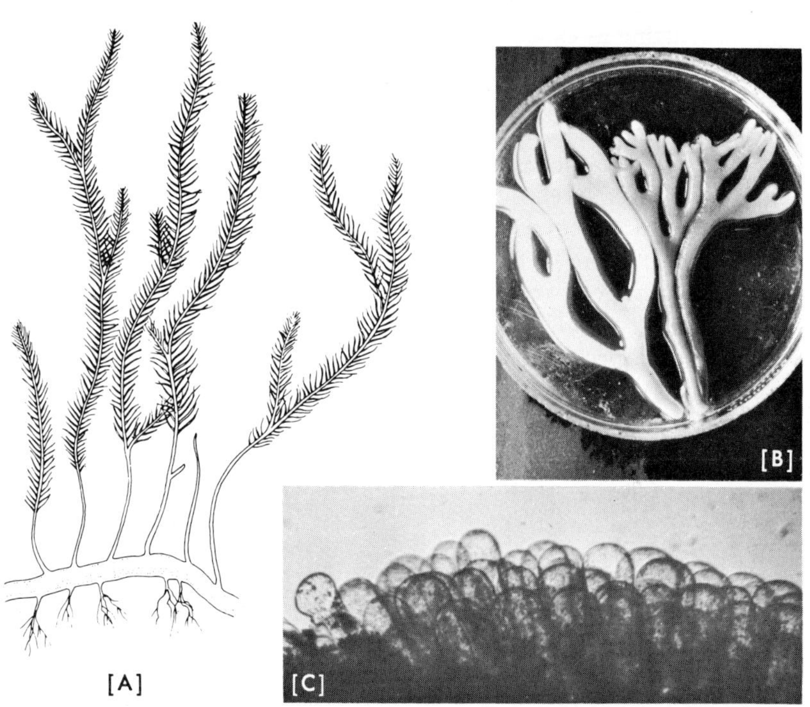

Figure 6·15. A: *Caulerpa* sp. **B,C:** *Codium* sp. **B** shows a portion of freshly collected plants in a Petri dish. **C** is a surface view of the plant showing pseudoparenchymatous organization.

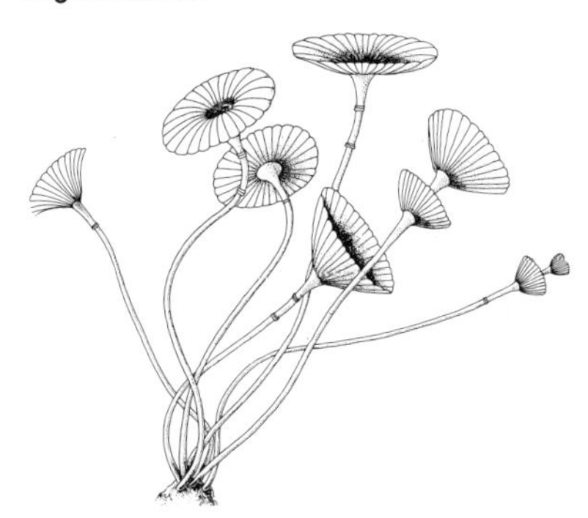

Figure 6·16. *Acetabularia* sp., mermaid's wine goblet. [After W. R. Taylor, *Marine Algae of the Eastern Tropical and Subtropical Coasts of the Americas,* Ann Arbor, Mich.: The University of Michigan Press, 1960, plate 4, fig. 5.]

Charophyta (Stoneworts)

The Charophyta, the stoneworts or brittleworts, although in many respects physiologically and biochemically like Chlorophycophyta (Table 5·1, page 26), differ from the latter so markedly in their morphology that they are often classified as a separate division as is done here. They are considered to have attributes which suggest an affinity to both algae and bryophytes (mosses and liverworts) but probably are not closely related to either.

Chara and *Nitella* are the most widespread representatives of the group, occurring as extensive colonies in clear-water lakes and streams. These plants are readily recognizable macroscopically because of their whorled organization (Figure 6·17) and length which may attain four feet. *Chara* and *Nitella* have apical growth and their axes and branches have clearly visible nodes and internodes. The latter are composed of single multinucleate cells with rather rapidly streaming cytoplasm. The internodes may be covered with corticating cells. The plants are anchored to the bottom by extensive **rhizoids** which give rise to numerous erect shoots in vegetative propagation.

The sexual reproductive structures (Figure 6·18) are quite complex. A majority of species are bisexual; the sex organs are borne at the nodes. The globular antheridium consists of sterile covering cells (shield cells) which enclose a tangled mass of colorless filaments, each cell of which produces a single sperm at maturity. The wall (shield)

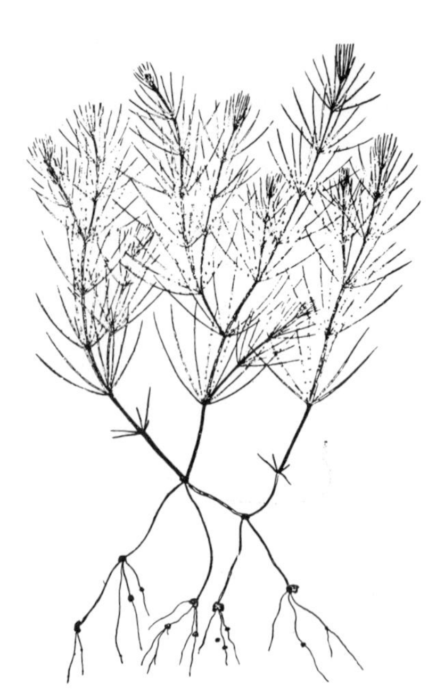

Figure 6·17. *Chara fragifera*. Habit of growth.

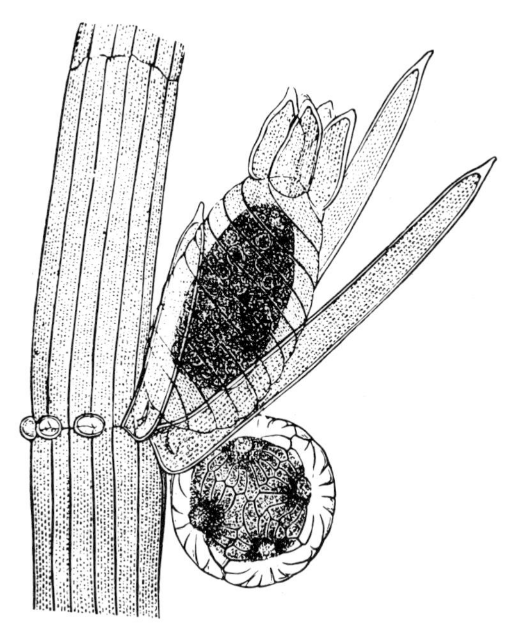

Figure 6·18. ***Chara*** **sp.** Sex organs—the oogonium with spiral cover cells (above) and the globular antheridium (below).

cells open when the sperms are mature. The oogonium which encloses a single egg cell is surrounded by five spirally twisted tube cells, the apices of which are delimited as five (*Chara*) or ten (*Nitella*) crown cells. After fertilization the mature zygotes [5] are shed. They germinate after a period of dormancy. The life cycle of these organisms is presumably type I (page 22), but further study of it is necessary to achieve certainty on this point.

Euglenophycophyta (Euglenoids)

The euglenoids are largely motile green flagellates which although having chlorophylls *a* and *b,* differ from the Chlorophycophyta with respect to their reserve foods (Table 5·1) and cellular organization. They are closely related to certain (colorless) flagellate protozoa, and the chlorophyllous forms can be induced by experimental procedures (heat, streptomycin, histamines) to lose their chlorophyll and to live heterotrophically. Approximately 25 genera and 400 species are known.

The best-known member, *Euglena* (Figure 6·19A–C) is widely dis-

[5] Usually called oospores.

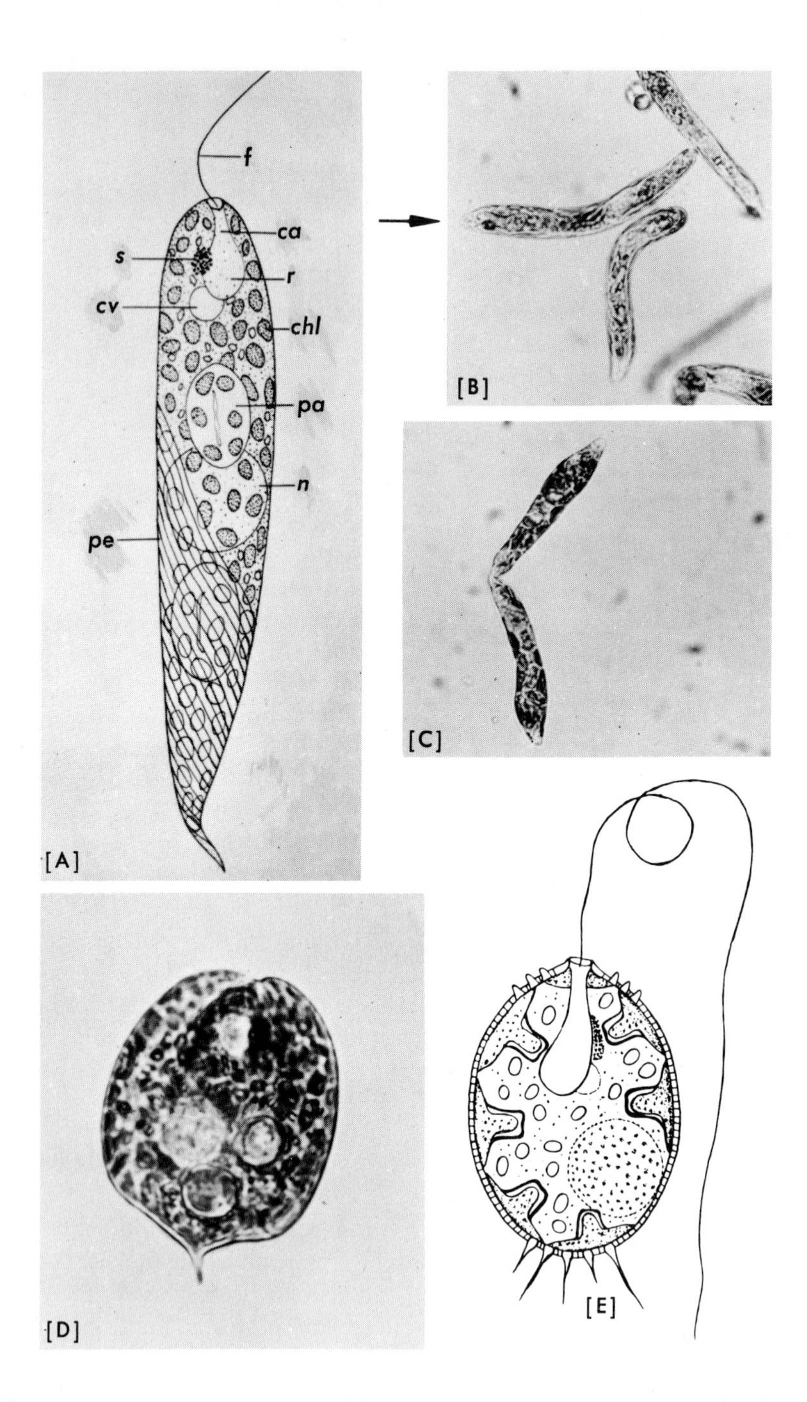

Figure 6·19. A–C: *Euglena.* **A:** Cellular organization. Code: *ca,* canal; *chl,* chloroplast; *cv,* contractile vacuole; *f,* flagellum; *n,* nucleus; *pa,* paramylum; *pe,* periplast; *r,* reservoir; and *s,* stigma. **B:** Photomicrograph of living cells—note red eyespots and short flagellum (on cell indicated by arrow). **C:** Reproduction in *Euglena.* **D:** *Phacus* species (flagellum not visible). **E:** *Trachelomonas* sp. [**A** from H. C. Bold, *Morphology of Plants,* New York: Harper & Row, 1957, p. 109; **E** courtesy of Dr. K. S. Singh.]

tributed and occurs both in fresh waters, where it frequently forms a velvety surface bloom or film, and in soil. Another species contains a red pigment, astaxanthin, which may mask the chlorophyll.

The cell in *Euglena* is pliable, not rigid, and the surface protoplasm is highly organized as a periplast. The emergent [6] flagellum is anchored at the base of a slightly subapical invagination, the reservoir and canal. Additional features of the cellular organization of *Euglena* are given in Figure 6·19A and in its caption.

Reproduction is by cell division. Encysted stages preserve the species during adverse environmental conditions. The occurrence of sexual reproduction has not been confirmed.

The related genera *Phacus* and *Trachelomonas* are illustrated in Figure 6·19D,E.

Xanthophycophyta (Yellow-Green Algae)

The members of this division, approximately 70 genera and 360 species, were included in the Chlorophycophyta until their distinctive pigmentation, storage products, and unequal flagellation (Table 5·1) became apparent. A number of these algae have two-part walls consisting of overlapping segments. The organization of the plant body in this group parallels in part that of the Chlorophycophyta in that both motile and nonmotile unicellular, colonial, filamentous and tubular genera are known.

Botrydiopsis (Figure 6·20) is an example of a unicellular type which corresponds to *Chlorococcum*-like organisms of the Chlorophycophyta. Its nonmotile, multinucleate spherical cells reproduce by zoospore formation; the zoospores have unequal flagella.

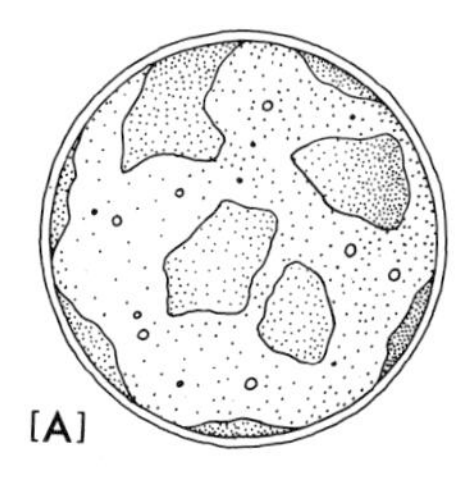

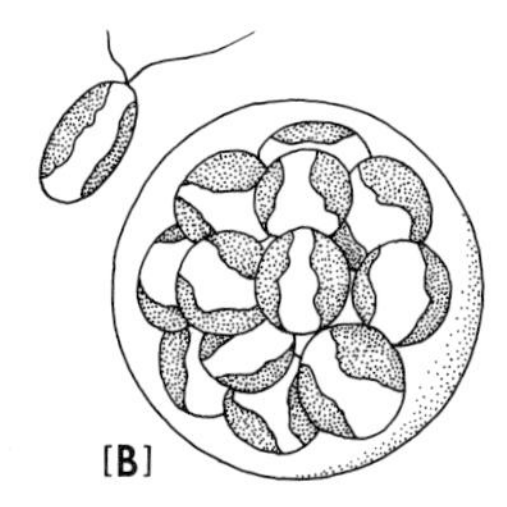

Figure 6·20. *Botrydiopsis arhiza*. A: Vegetative cell. **B:** Zoosporangium and zoospore. [From H. C. Bold, *Morphology of Plants,* New York: Harper & Row, 1957, p. 116.]

The filamentous *Tribonema* (Figure 6·21) is superficially similar to *Ulothrix* of the green algal group. In *Tribonema* the walls of the cells of the unbranched filaments are composed of two slightly overlapping "H-shaped pieces," actually in three dimensions, like two water tum-

[6] A second, very short flagellum does not emerge from the reservoir.

blers. Reproduction of *Tribonema* is by zoospore formation (Figure 6·21C).

The saclike *Botrydium* (Figure 6·22A), a common soil alga suggests both *Protosiphon* and certain of the tubular, siphonalean green algae. The vesicles of *Botrydium* may attain 1.5 mm in length and are

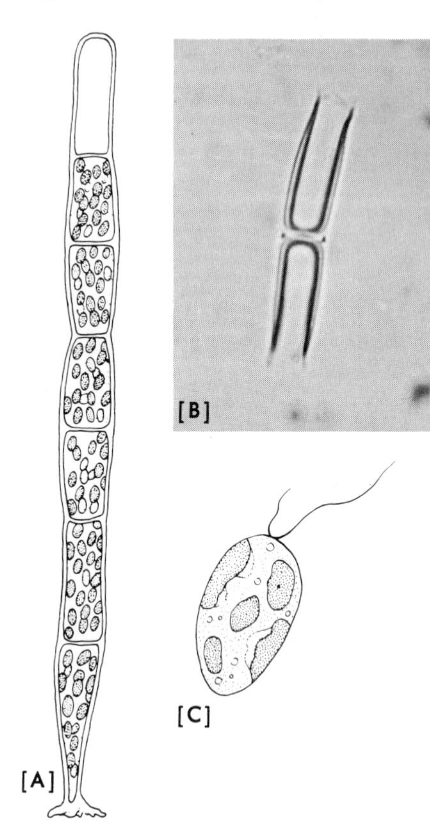

Figure 6·21. *Tribonema* sp. A: Single filament attached by holdfast. **B:** H-shaped wall segment. **C:** Zoospore.

highly vacuolate. The peripheral layer of protoplasm contains many small, lenslike chloroplasts and numerous nuclei. Reproduction when adequate moisture is present is by unequally flagellate zoospores which may also function as isogametes. The thick-walled cysts and nonmotile aplanospores of *Botrydium* are able to withstand desiccation. The life cycle of *Botrydium* is probably type I (page 22).

Vaucheria (Figure 6·22B,C), the "water felt," is a well-known member of the Xanthophycophyta which is widely distributed on moist soil and in both quiet and rapidly running waters. Both marine and freshwater species are known. The tubular plant body is sparingly branched. Sexual reproduction is oogamous (Figure 6·22C), the oogonia and antheridia occurring as lateral protuberances. The life cycle of *Vaucheria* is probably type I (page 22).

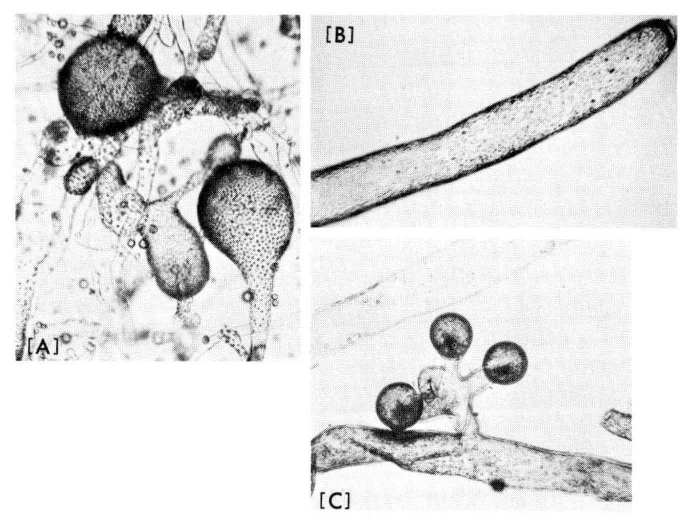

Figure 6·22. **A:** *Botrydium* sp. in culture. **B,C:** *Vaucheria* sp. **B:** Apex of one vegetative siphon or tube. **C:** Sex organs, consisting of three oogonia and one curved antheridium on a lateral branch.

Chrysophycophyta (Golden Algae)

The Chrysophycophyta include a number of unicellular and colonial and flagellate and amoeboid algae with pseudopodial extensions of the protoplasm. The plastids are varying shades of brown. Many members of the division have the capacity to form siliceous or carbonaceous walls which cover the vegetative cells or the encysted forms. Three types of flagellation occur: biflagellate, unequally biflagellate, and uniflagellate. Approximately 75 genera and 300 species have been described.

Ochromonas (Figure 6·23A), one species of which is versatile in

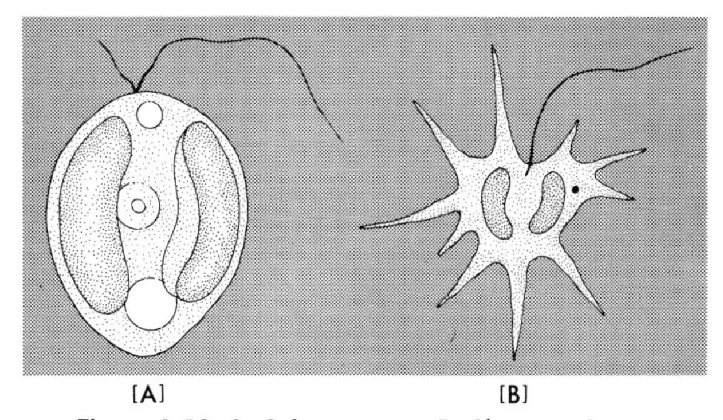

Figure 6·23. **A:** *Ochromonas* sp. **B:** *Chrysamoeba* sp.

nutrition (it may grow photoautotrophically, heterotrophically, or phagotrophically) is a unicellular organism with unequal flagellation. *Chrysamoeba* (Figure 6·23B) is an amoeboid species with pseudopodia.

An interesting series of Chrysophycophyta, mostly marine planktonic organisms, have minute discs or rings of calcium carbonate embedded in the outer layer of their cell envelopes (Figure 6·24A). The calcareous ornaments are known as **coccoliths.**

Synura (Figure 6·24B) and *Dinobryon* (Figure 6·24C) are widely distributed members of the freshwater plankton. In the spherical or ellipsoidal colonies of *Synura* the individual, equally biflagellate cells radiate from a center. The cells are covered with siliceous plates and each contains two plastids.

The unequally flagellate cells of *Dinobryon* are contained in bell-shaped structures, the loricas. After cell division either one or both products of division may leave the parent lorica and secrete a new one. In this way, arborescent colonies are built up.

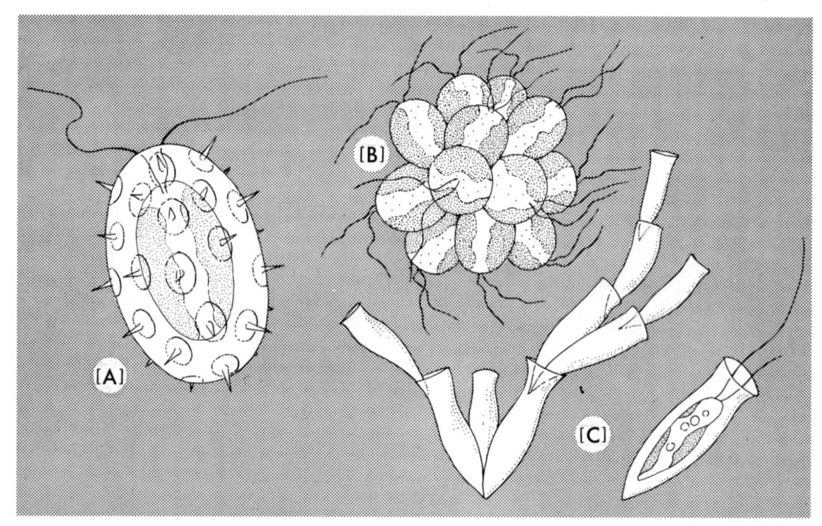

Figure 6·24. **A:** *Syracosphaera* sp. **B:** *Synura* sp. **C:** *Dinobryon* sp., arborescent colony at left, single cell at right. [**B** from H. C. Bold, *Morphology of Plants,* New York: Harper & Row, 1957, p. 123; **C** from G. M. Smith, *Freshwater Algae of the United States,* New York: McGraw-Hill, 1950, p. 424.]

Bacillariophycophyta (Diatoms)

Diatoms are organisms of great biological and economic importance (page 65). Both marine and freshwater and planktonic and benthic forms occur, and of the latter, a number are epiphytic on other aquatic vegetation. About 200 genera and 5,000 species of diatoms are known.

Diatoms are unicellular, colonial, or filamentous in organization. Two major series may be distinguished on the basis of their symmetry (and other features) : the pennate and centric diatoms. In the former,

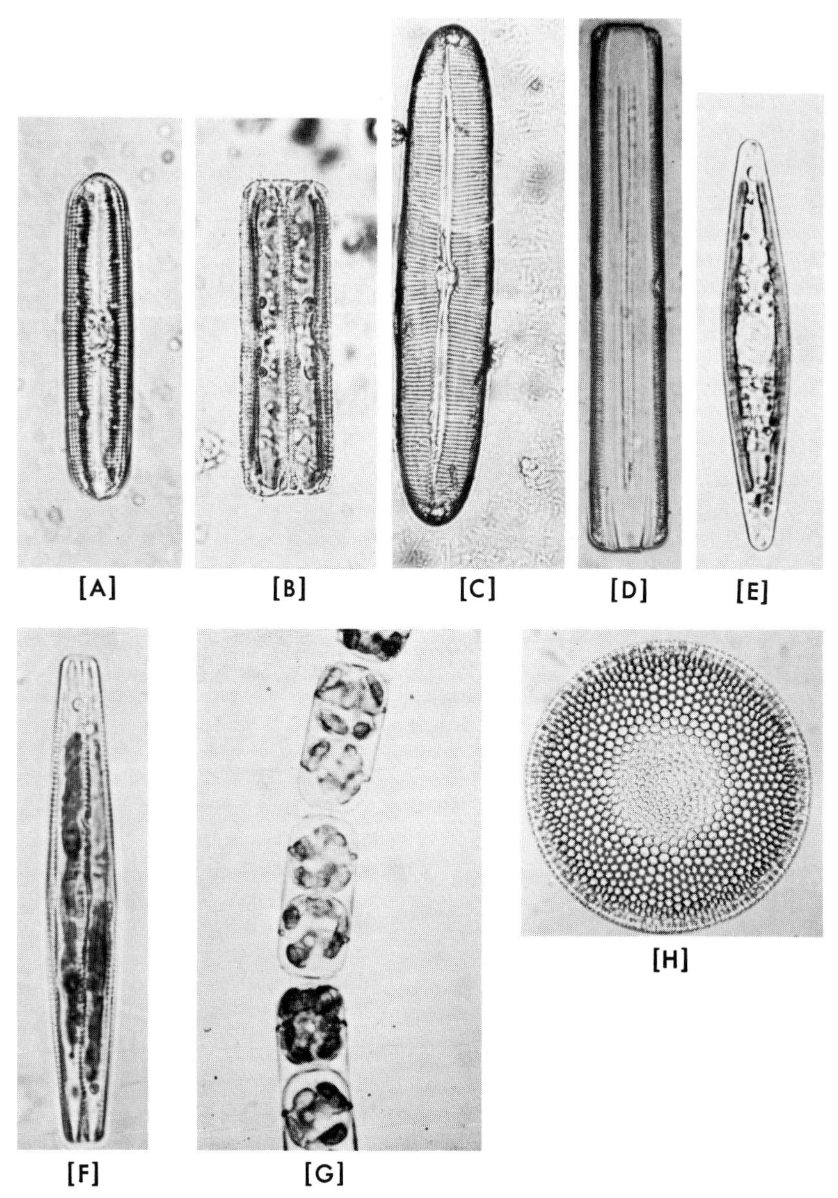

Figure 6·25. Diatoms. A: Valve view of living *Pinnularia.* **B:** Girdle view of *Pinnularia* at conclusion of cell division. **C:** "Cleaned" frustule, valve view. **D:** "Cleaned" frustule of *Pinnularia* in girdle view. **E:** Living *Navicula* in valve view. **F:** Recently divided *Navicula* in girdle view. **G:** *Melosira* sp. **H:** *Coscinodiscus* sp., centric diatoms.

the symmetry is bilateral (Figure 6·25A–F), while in the latter it is radial (Figure 6·25G,H).

The cell walls of diatoms are pectic and contain also silicon dioxide. The taxonomy of the group is based almost exclusively on the form and ornamentation of the cell walls. It is usually advantageous to heat the cells in nitric or other acids to dissolve the cell contents in order to get a clearer view of the details of wall ornamentation—often beautiful and extremely complex (Figure 6·25H).

Each diatom is enclosed by two slightly overlapping walls (Figures 6·24, 26), or **valves,** called **frustules** by diatomists. The larger is the **epitheca** and the smaller, the **hypotheca.** In three dimensions these cell walls are boxlike, either rectangular or pillbox-like, or they may be like two slightly overlapping glass tumblers. The boxlike frustules may be observed in face or valve view (Figures 6·25A,C,E; 6·26A) or in edge or girdle view (Figures 6·25B,D,F; 6·26B). In certain pennate diatoms, one or both valves may have a fissure or **raphe** (Figures 6·25C; 6·26A); such diatoms are motile although the mechanism of the motility is not completely understood.

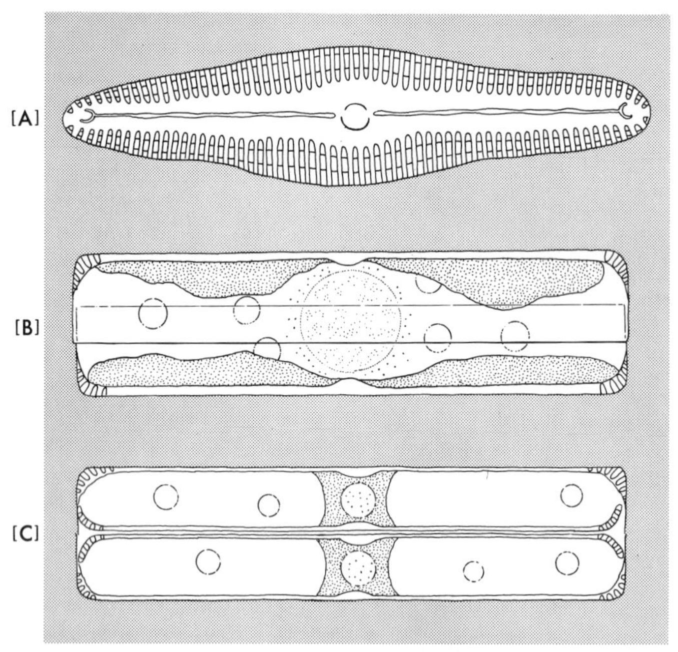

Figure 6·26. Cellular organization of the diatom *Pinnularia*. A: Surface view of frustule—note raphe and central and polar nodules. **B:** Living cell of *Pinnularia* in girdle view—note massive chloroplasts, central nucleus, and overlapping of valves. **C:** *Pinnularia*, girdle view of recently divided cell. [From H. C. Bold, *Morphology of Plants,* New York: Harper & Row, 1957, p. 128.]

Diatom cells have prominent, single nuclei and massive ribbonlike or lenslike plastids. The plastids contain a distinctive combination of pigments and produce oils and chrysolaminarin (Table 5·1).

In cell division, which results in the multiplication of the unicellular forms and growth in the colonial and filamentous forms of diatoms, mitotic nuclear division is followed by division of the cytoplasm. New half-walls (valves) are then secreted; both the original epitheca and hypotheca serve as epithecas for the new products of cell division (Figures 6·25B,F; 6·26C). Although one-half the progeny of each division thus is slightly smaller, marked reduction in size of individuals in a population does not always occur because of flexibility in the newly forming cell walls.

Both pennate and centric diatoms are presumably diploid organisms and type II (page 22) in life cycle. Sexual reproduction is preceded by meiosis which is followed by organization of one or two gametes by each pairing cell of pennate diatoms (Figure 6·27) so that one or two zygotes are formed. The zygotes of diatoms are called **auxospores** because of their increase in size in forming vegetative cells.

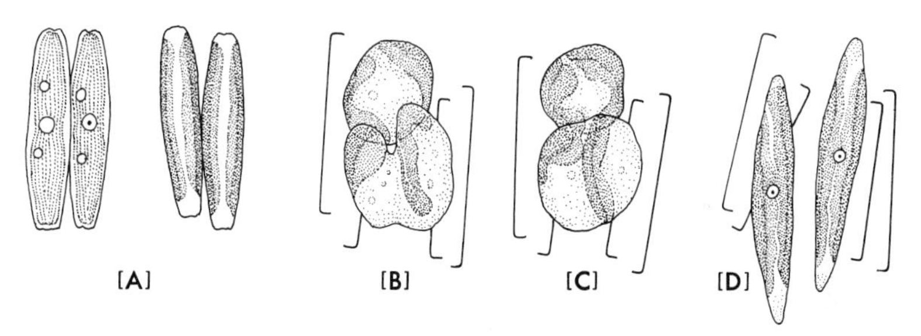

Figure 6·27. Sexual reproduction in *Navicula halophila*. **A:** Paired cells in early sexual reproduction. **B:** One zygote and one pair of gametes in act of fusion. **C:** Two zygotes formed. **D:** Elongation of zygotes (auxospores) to form vegetative cells. [From R. Subrahmanyan, in *M.O.P. Iyengar Commemoration Volume*, Indian Botanical Society: 239–266, 1947.]

In the centric diatoms either nuclear union follows meiosis within a given cell, or reproduction is oogamous, the sperms being minute and uniflagellate.

Phaeophycophyta (Brown Algae)

Unlike most groups of algae which have both marine and fresh-water representatives, the brown algae are almost exclusively marine and attached benthic forms. Approximately 230 genera and 1,500 species have been described. The distinctive attributes of brown algae are cited in Table 5·1.

The simplest brown algae known are filamentous such as *Ectocarpus* (Figure 6·28), which is widespread in marine habitats, attached either to stones and pilings or to other aquatic vegetation. The cells of *Ectocarpus* contain undulate, ribbon-like brown plastids and are uninucleate. Its life cycle is type III (page 22). The haploid, laterally biflagellate zoospores are produced following meiosis in the unilocular zoosporangium (Figure 6·28B) specially differentiated from the vegetative cells. These grow into haploid sexual plants which produce the gametes in finger-like plurilocular gametangia (Figure 6·28C,D); the gametes (Figure 6·28E) also are laterally biflagellate. The motile zygotes develop into the zoospore-producing plants.

The largest and most complex organisms classified as algae are the brown algae known as **kelps** (Figures 6·29, 6·30). These grow in the subtidal zone in cold waters on the rocky Atlantic and Pacific Oceans and other similar coasts throughout the world. The kelp plant, which is diploid, may exceed 150 feet in length in such a genus as *Macrocystis* (Figure 6·29A,B). In a majority of kelps the plant consists of a massive branching attaching organ, the holdfast, stem or stipe and a blade. The stipe may branch and form a number of blades.

The kelps are complex histologically (Figure 6·30A). The blade has cells densely filled with plastids on both surfaces with larger cells below and filamentous cells in the center or medulla. In the stipes of three genera there occur sieve tubes similar to those which are found in the phloem of vascular plants. Although it has not yet been demonstrated that organic substances are translocated in the sieve tubes, isotopic techniques have demonstrated movement of such substances in the stipe.

In reproduction, dense patches of unilocular zoosporangia and associated paraphyses (Figure 6·30B,C) develop on the surface of the kelp blade. The liberated zoospores attach to rocks where they develop into male and female gametophytes (Figure 6·30D,E). The latter are oogamous. The eggs are fertilized at the mouths of the oogonia, and the resultant zygotes develop young sporophytes with rhizoids which anchor them to the rocky substrate (Figure 6·30F,G). The life cycle of the kelps, accordingly, is type III (page 22), with extreme contrast in size between the alternants.

The rockweeds comprise a third group of brown algae widespread on rocky shores often in the intertidal zone. *Fucus, Ascophyllum, Pelvetia,* and *Sargassum* are members of this group. While most of these plants are attached, a great floating population of *Sargassum natans* occurs in that part of the Atlantic Ocean known as the Sargasso Sea.

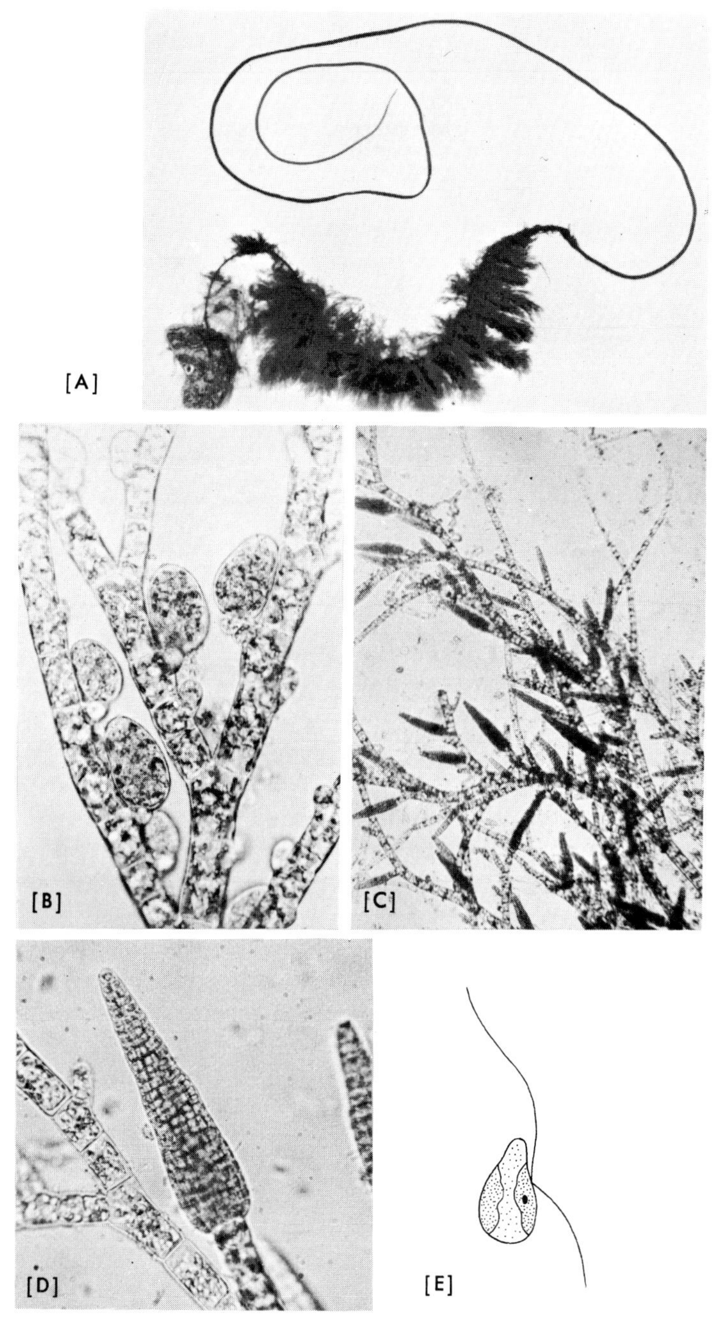

Figure 6·28. ***Ectocarpus.*** **A:** Filamentous plants of *Ectocarpus* growing on the shoestring kelp, *Chorda filum*. **B:** Plant with unilocular zoosporangia. **C:** Plant with plurilocular reproductive structures, probably gametangia. **D:** Plurilocular reproductive structure enlarged. **E:** Gamete.

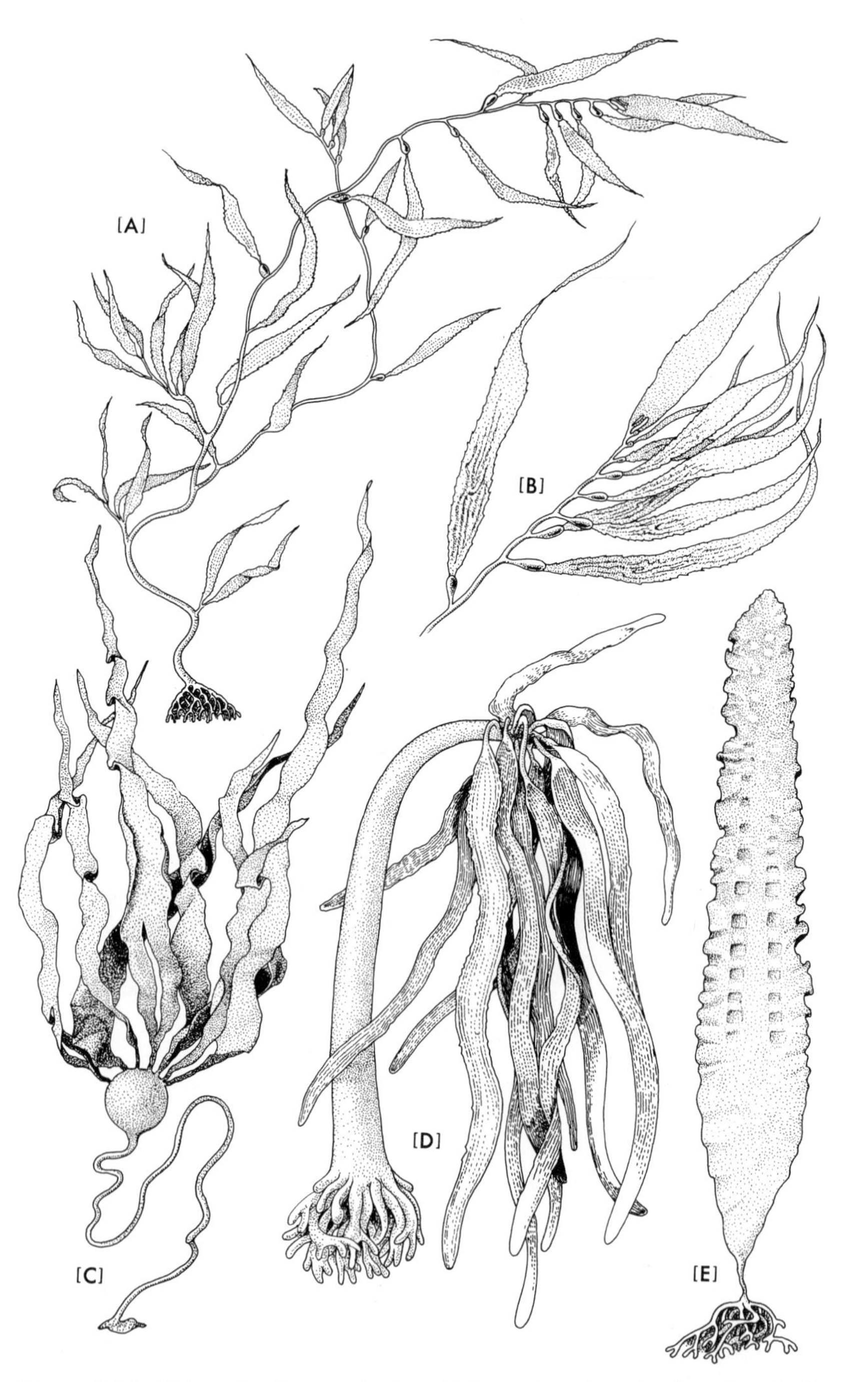

Figure 6·29. Kelps. A: *Macrocystis integrifolia,* entire plant (much reduced). **B:** Upper portion of a branch (also much reduced). **C:** *Nereocystis luetkeana.* **D:** *Postelsia palmaeformis,* the sea palm. **E:** *Laminaria agardhii.* (See also Figure 6·28A.) [**E** from H. C. Bold, *Morphology of Plants,* New York: Harper & Row, 1957, p. 74.]

Fucus (Figure 6·31) is a dichotomously branching, bladelike plant attached to rocky shores by disclike holdfasts. At maturity the tips become enlarged as fertile receptacles (Figure 6·31A). The oogonia and antheridia are borne in chambers or conceptacles on these receptacles (Figure 6·31C,D). Both unisexual and bisexual plants occur, according to the species. The mature oogonia and antheridia are liberated from the conceptacles when the plants are exposed at low tide. As they become submerged, the liberated sex organs are washed into the water where they, in turn, shed their eggs and sperm (Figure 6·31E). The zygotes attach to rocks and rapidly develop into new *Fucus* plantlets (Figure 6·31F). The life cycle of the rockweeds is type II (page 22).

Rhodophycophyta (Red Algae)

Although similar to the Cyanophycophyta in pigmentation and lack of flagellate cells, the red algae are eukaryotic and, furthermore, markedly different in their plant bodies and reproduction. Approximately 400 genera and 1,500 species of red algae are known of which the great majority are marine algae of warmer waters, although more than 200 species occur in fresh water. Among the latter, *Batrachospermum, Lemanea,* and *Compsopogon* are rather widespread. Certain of the distinguishing characteristics of the red algae have been presented in Table 5·1. In addition, it should be added that the cells of many red algae have common pit connections between their walls, the structure and function of which are only now being elucidated through electron microscopy. The morphology of their organs of sexual reproduction further distinguish them.

The female gametangium, here called the **carpogonium,** consists of a basal uninucleate region which functions as an egg and a more or less prominent receptive protuberance, the **trichogyne** (Figure 6·32G). The carpogonium is often borne on a modified, almost colorless branch, the carpogonial branch.

The male gametes, here called **spermatia,** are produced singly in unicellular gametangia designated **spermatangia** (Figure 6·32F). The spermatia, some of which are slightly amoeboid, are colorless or almost so.

Various types of spores also are produced by red algae. Clearly asexual spores may be produced singly (monospores) or in greater numbers from vegetative cells or special sporangia. The classical **tetraspores** arise following meiosis in tetrasporangia (Figures 6·33; 6·34D). Carposporangia and carpospores (Figure 6·32H) also occur in the life cycle. Carpospores (haploid or diploid) arise as a result of fertilization.

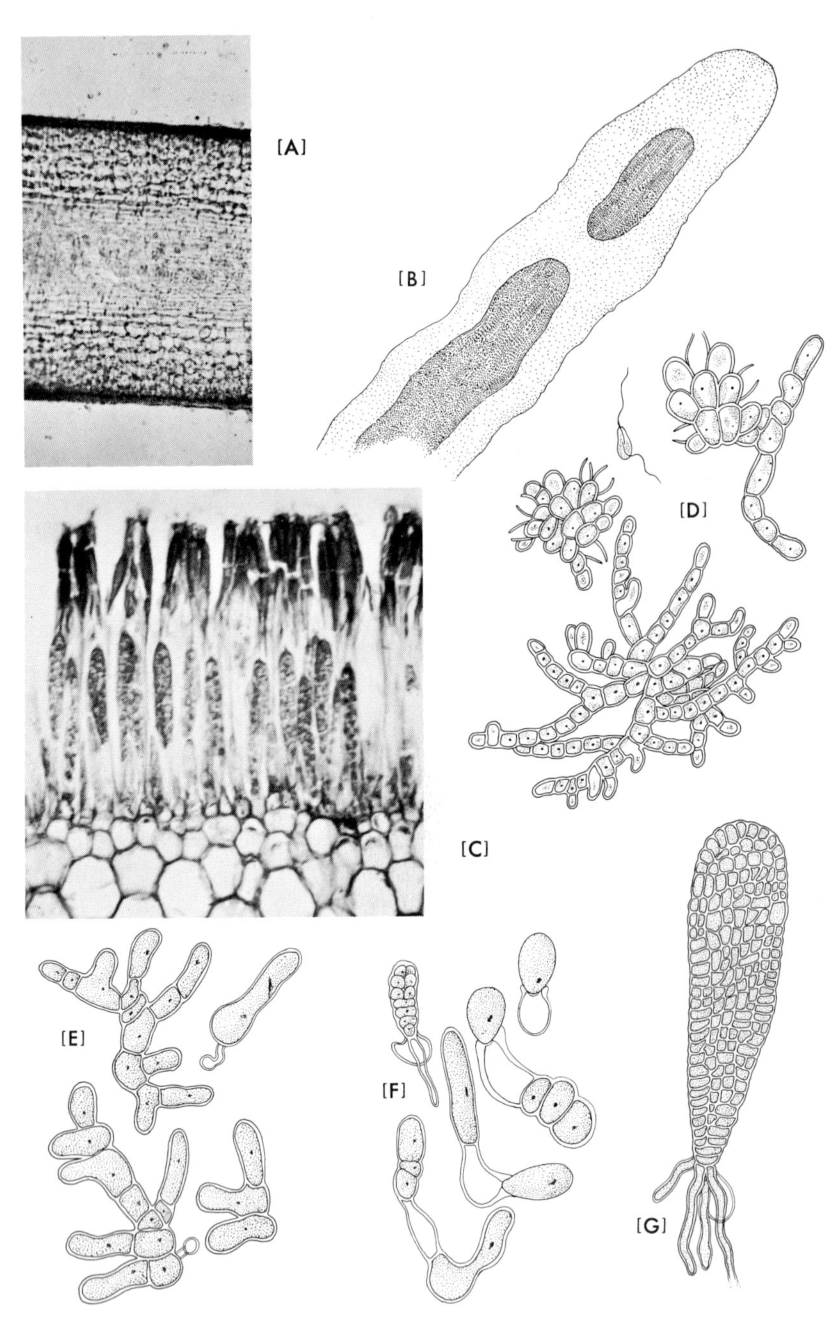

Figure 6·30. A: Transection of kelp blade. The dark regions above and below represent superficial cells rich in chloroplasts. Note central medulla and cortical regions on either side. **B:** Segment of a fertile blade of kelp (*Laminaria*). The dark area indicates location of unilocular zoosporangia. **C:** Portion of a transection of a fertile kelp blade—note elongate, unilocular zoosporangia. **D:** Three male gametophytes of *Laminaria* sp.—note terminal antheridia, some of them empty, and single sperm. **E:** Female gametophytes of *Laminaria* sp. in various stages of development. Cells with

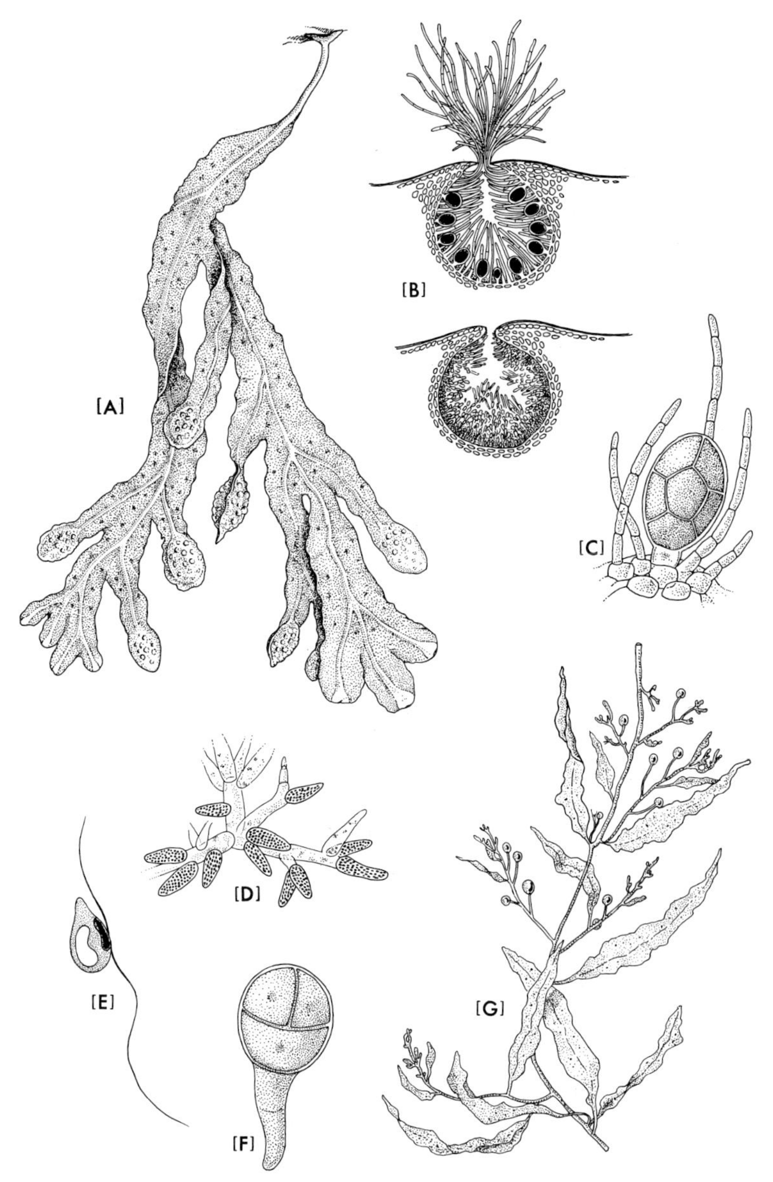

Figure 6·31. *Fucus* sp., a rockweed. A: Habit of growth. **B:** Transection of male (below) and female (above) conceptacles. **C:** Oogonium containing eight eggs; surrounding filaments are paraphyses. **D:** Branching antheridial filament from male conceptacle. **E:** Single sperm. **F:** *Sargassum filipendula.*

---

protuberances are young oogonia. **F:** Female gametophytes showing extruded eggs at fertilization and (at the left) two early stages in the development of the sporophyte. **G:** Young sporophyte of *Laminaria* sp. [**D–G** from T. Kanda, in Scientific Papers of the Institute of Algalogical Research, Faculty of Science, Hokkaido Imperial Univ. 1, 1936.]

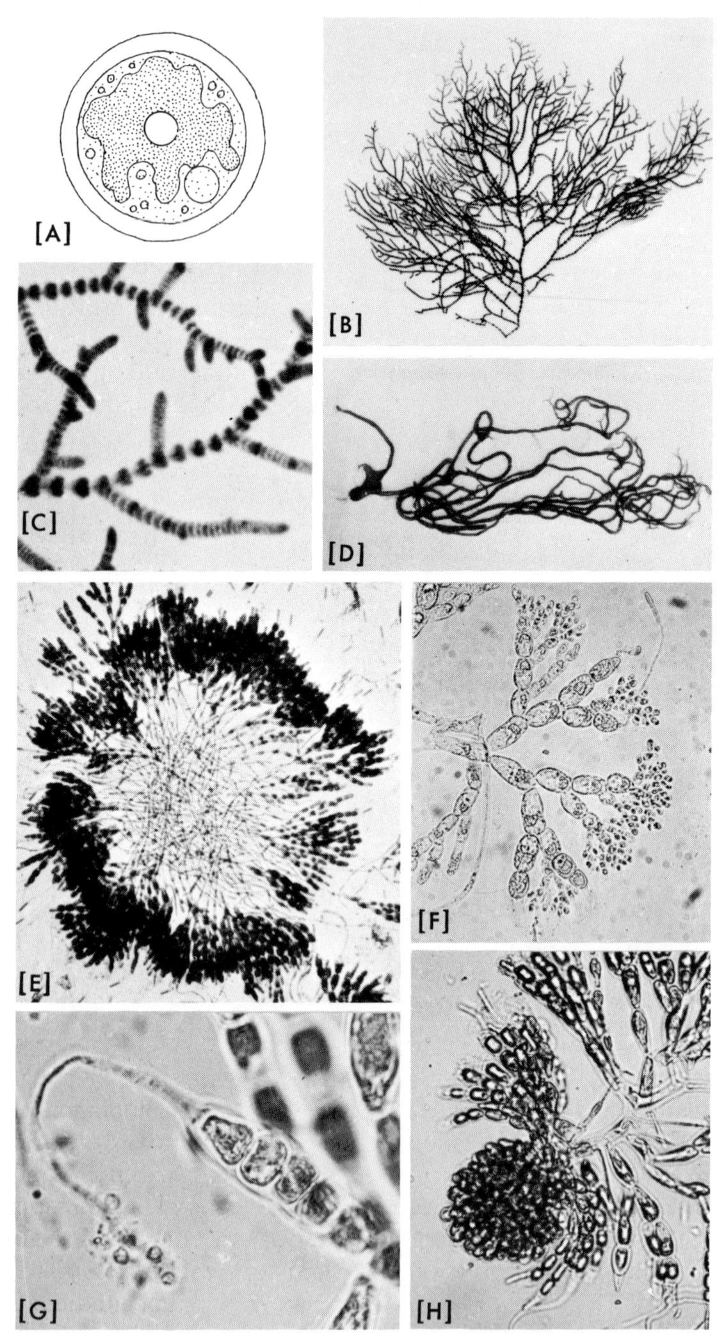

Figure 6·32. A: *Porphyridium cruentum.* **B,C:** *Batrachospermum.* **D–H:** *Nemalion multifidum.* **D:** Habit of growth. **E:** Transection—note colorless axial filaments supporting photosynthetic ones. **F:** Branch with spermatangia. **G:** Carpogonial branch at fertilization—note spermatia attached to trichogyne. **H:** Mass of carposporangia arising after fertilization.

Several unicellular red algae are known, among them, *Porphyridium; P. cruentum* (Figure 6·32A) occurs as blood red patches on moist soils. Its sole method of reproduction apparently is by cell division.

Nemalion and *Batrachospermum* (Figure 6·32B–H) are classical types among Rhodophycophyta, the former marine and the latter fresh-water. In *Nemalion* the plant axis consists of a number of elongate colorless filaments which produce tufts of bead-shaped photosynthetic filaments on all sides. *Batrachospermum* has a single longitudinal axial filament. The life cycle in both genera is reported to be type I (page 22). The haploid carpospores, which are produced in clusters (Figure 6·32H) following fertilization of each carpogonial branch, germinate upon their release into branching filaments which presumably give rise to the typical plants of *Nemalion* and *Batrachospermum*.

Polysiphonia (Figure 6·33) and *Griffithsia* (Figure 6·34) illustrate

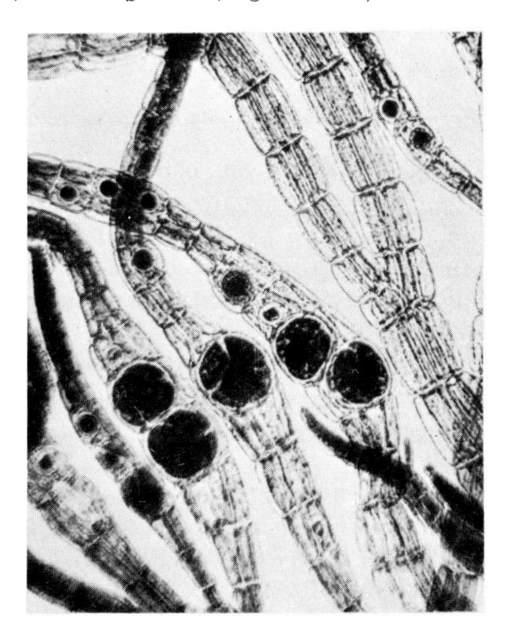

Figure 6·33. *Polysiphonia* sp., tetrasporic plant.

the diplobiontic type of life cycle among Rhodophycophyta in which diploid tetrasporic plants occur in the life cycle. In both genera the individual plants are unisexual (Figure 6·34A,B): the spermatia and carpogonia occur on different haploid plants. As a result of fertilization, which is not followed immediately by meiosis, diploid carposporangia (Figure 6·34C) are produced. These develop, after they have been shed, into diploid tetrasporophytes (Figure 6·34D) which produce haploid tetraspores. Two members of each tetrad presumably develop into male plants and two into female. The life cycle of typical diplobiontic red algae is summarized below. (The diploid phases are printed in boldface type.)

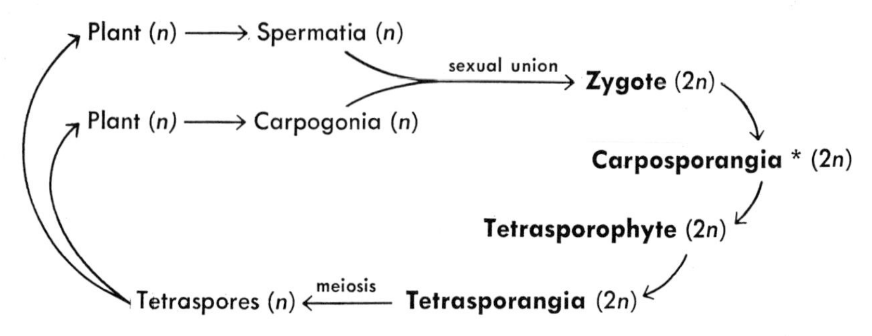

* The group of carpospores is sometimes collectively called the carposporophyte.

The life cycle is fundamentally type III (page 22) with the insertion of the *diploid* carposporophyte between the zygote and the free-living diploid plant (tetrasporophyte).

Pyrrophycophyta (in part, Dinoflagellates)

The dinoflagellates contain motile flagellate, nonmotile unicellular, and filamentous representatives. Approximately 100 genera and 900 species are known. They are clearly related to a large assemblage of colorless organisms with similar organization, classified among the protozoa.

Certain distinctive attributes of the group have been summarized in Table 5·1.

Motile dinoflagellates exemplified by *Ceratium* and *Peridinium* are various shades of brown and have prominent red eyespots. The cell surface is covered by a series of plates (Figure 6·35) reported to be cellulosic. The most conspicuous distinguishing attribute of dinoflagellates is the presence of a transverse furrow which divides the cell into equal or rather unequal semicells (Figure 6·35). From an opening in the furrow emerge two flagella. One of these merely undulates in the furrow, while the other is posterior.

Reproduction is largely by cell division, although occurrence of sexual union of individuals has been reported several times.

The role of dinoflagellates in red tides has been alluded to on page 2.

Cryptophycophyta (Cryptomonads)

The cryptomonads are a small assemblage of flagellates generally unicellular; the cells are biflagellate and flattened (Figure 6·36). The

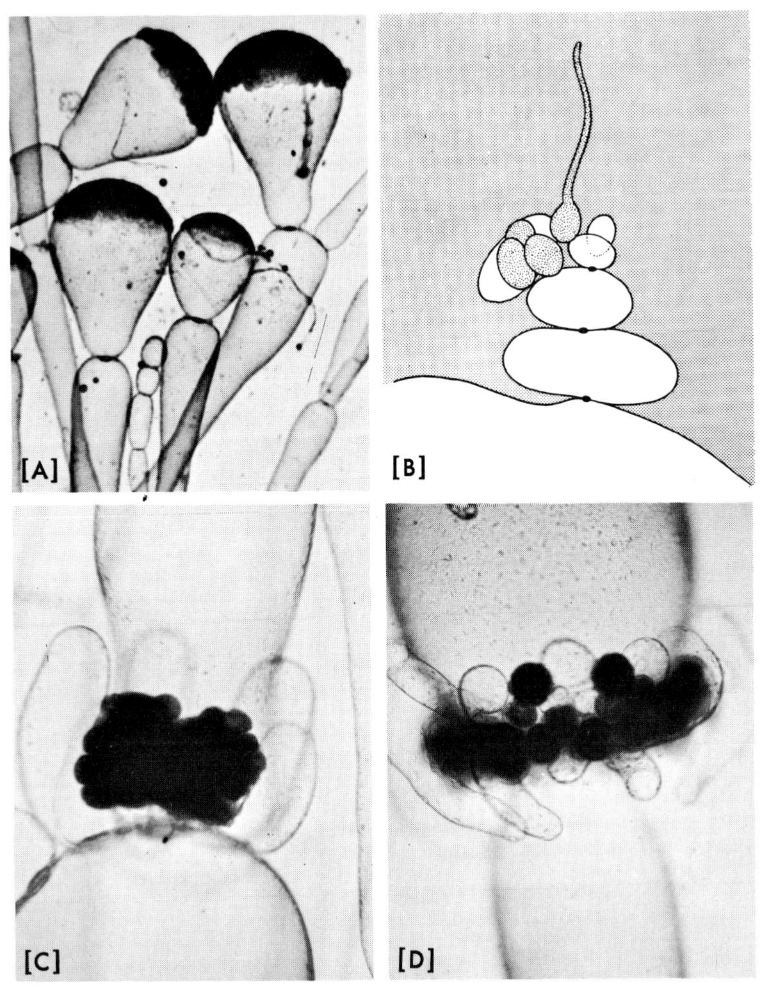

Figure 6·34. ***Griffithsia globulifera.*** **A:** Male plants with spermatangial caps. **B:** Carpogonial branch (stippled). **C:** Cystocarp, consisting of carpospores and surrounding sterile cells. **D:** Node of tetrasporophyte with ring of tetrasporangia and sterile cells. [**A, C, D** from H. C. Bold, *Morphology of Plants,* New York: Harper & Row, 1957, p. 98.]

cells may be naked or walled and the flagella emerge from a gullet. Their distinctive pigments have been summarized in Table 5·1. Starch is the storage product in many forms. Each cell contains two curved brownish plastids. Nonmotile cryptomonads may occur in gelatinous matrices and may revert to the motile condition under special environmental conditions.

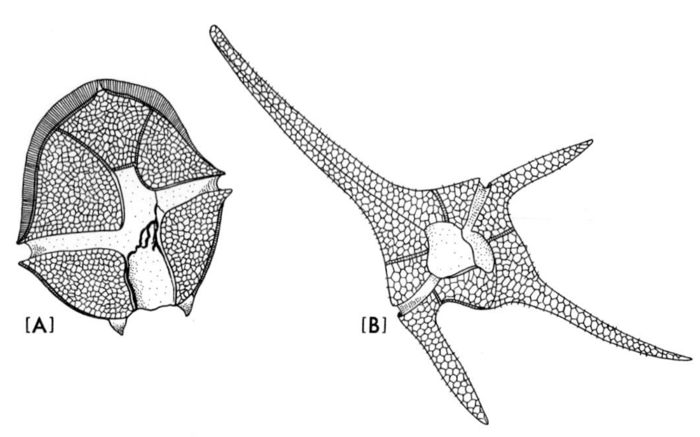

Figure 6·35. Dinoflagellates. A: *Peridinium* sp. **B:** *Ceratium* sp. (cell contents and flagella not shown). [After L. H. Tiffany and M. E. Britton, *The Algae of Illinois*, plate 85, Office of Naval Research, 1952.]

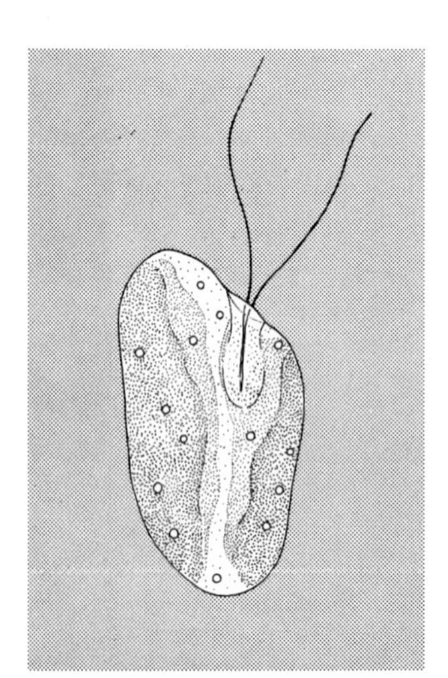

Figure 6·36. ***Cryptomonas*** **sp.**

CHAPTER

7

Economic and Biological Significance of Algae

THE PRECEDING CHAPTERS dealing with algae have concerned primarily the algae themselves with respect to their organization and activities. It remains now to consider two additional aspects of algae: their relation to the world's economy, and thus to man, and their biological significance. These two topics, of course, are not mutually exclusive.

Economic Aspects

In appraising the role of algae in our economy, our thoughts may be brought into sharp focus by examining the proposition as to what results would obtain were algae to be somehow totally eradicated from their various habitats.

The most striking and direct effects would soon be discernible in all aquatic animal life which would be deprived of its indispensable primary food source and thus would no longer be able to exist. Aquatic algae then are to aquatic animals what green pastures are to herbivores, although the relationship is sometimes not as obvious or direct. While some animals such as certain protozoa, copepods, molluscs and fish (gizzard, shad and hake) feed directly on algae, others depend only indirectly (but nonetheless ultimately) on algae since they are carnivores.

The increasingly widespread practice of obtaining proteins in the form of fish for human consumption by constructing farm tanks and ponds has been successful insofar as an adequate supply of algae (especially planktonic species) are maintained. This is effected by periodic addition of inorganic fertilizer in much the same way that the latter is applied to terrestrial crops.

Human nutrition in maritime countries, especially in the Orient, has long been supplemented with various seaweeds; close to one hundred species have been used as food. The classical example, perhaps, is the cultivation and harvesting of the red alga *Porphyra* ("purple laver") by the Japanese.

Colloidal extracts of marine algae have long been used in and as foods. The carrageenin of *Chondrus crispus* (Irish Moss) is used in preparing puddings and another red alga (*Rhodymenia palmata*), "dulse," is used in various ways as a food supplement. More than 3,000,000 pounds (dry weight) of *Chondrus* were harvested for extraction from the rocky waters near Nova Scotia in 1960 and in the same year some 285,000 metric tons of seaweed were harvested in Japan.

Uses of extracts from marine brown (kelps and rockweeds) and red algae are increasing steadily. Alginic acid (from brown algae) and the agars, carrageenin and gelans of red algae are now widely used as thickenings, binders, and packing media in foods and as cloth-sizing agents and in a variety of medicinal applications. The use of agar as a solidifying agent in culture media, which began in the late nineteenth century, was a real "breakthrough" in microbiological technique because agar is not metabolized by most microorganisms as is gelatine which was used previously. Marine Phaeophycophyta, furthermore, are excellent sources of iodine and potash which they are able to accumulate in higher concentrations than are present in sea water.

In contrast to the large marine algae, the minute (approximately 5–10 μ) green alga *Chlorella* (and similar forms) has for two decades been used in pilot studies designed to explore its value as a food source for animals and humans. By experimental procedures it is possible to vary the proportions of lipids, carbohydrates and proteins within the cells to maxima of 85, 37, and 88.2 per cent, respectively. At present, although the food values are excellent, the cost of production of algal protein, carbohydrates and lipids is too high to allow for commercial production. Understandably, the Japanese are working actively in this area of applied physiological phycology.

It is also increasingly clear that algae both in culture and in nature are producing extracellular products which are important in microbial nutrition and ecology. These substances include polysaccharides and enzymes (amylase and proteases) and other nitrogenous compounds. Such secretions must have important effects on other microorganisms in the flora. For example, some of these extracellular products are antibiotic with respect to bacteria, as in the case of a product of *Anabaena cylindrica* which decreases the toxic effects of the bacterial secretion, polymyxin B, upon the alga.

The productivity of algae, of course, is based on their photosynthetic activities as a by-product of which, as in terrestrial green plants, oxygen is liberated. Although the oxygen content of the surface layers of natural waters is largely supplied by the atmosphere and enhanced turbulence, the algae play an important role in microhabitats, in relation to the organisms near or in contact with their surfaces. The oxygenation of waters by algae is exploited especially in sewage-treatment lagoons, where the algae (during daylight hours) augment the oxygen supply for the oxidative bacteria which destroy organic complexes. Of course, at night, the algae compete with the bacteria for available oxygen.

Finally, an economically important function of algae is that of nitrogen fixation which is performed by certain blue-green algae, both free-living and endophytic. The nitrogen-fixing blue-green algae, among other species of *Anabaena* and *Nostoc,* can grow in the absence of combined nitrogen and use gaseous nitrogen in their metabolism, as do the nitrogen-fixing bacteria. The presence of nitrogen-fixing blue-green algae has an important role in rice culture. It has been reported that rice fields inoculated with the nitrogen-fixing *Tolypothrix tenuis* after four years were producing 128% more crop than the uninoculated fields. Furthermore, the plants from the inoculated fields contained 7.5 lb more nitrogen per acre than the controls. The species *Anabaena* endophytic in the roots of certain cycads have been shown to be nitrogen fixers.

In addition to living algae, nonliving algae or their remains are valuable for certain purposes. In rocky islands and coastal areas kelps and other coarse algae are incorporated into the soil as fertilizer and to improve its water-holding capacity. Of tremendous value are the frustules of diatoms which are recovered from exposed deposits and from lake bottoms and used as diatomaceous earth for a number of purposes. These include, among others, absorptive packing around acid containers, as agents of filtration, as insulation, in the prevention of mine explosions, in paints, and in silver polish.

In addition to these beneficial activities of algae, certain deleterious ones must now be cited. Other than their adverse impact aesthetically, great masses of floating filamentous algae interfere with fishing and swimming. Furthermore, such masses and dense blooms of algae, when they blanket the water surface, may result in the death of aquatic animals since both algae and the fauna are competing for oxygen in darkness. Certain planktonic algae like *Chlamydomonas, Synura* and the diatom, *Asterionella,* impart characteristic tastes to water supplies as do blooms of algae when they disintegrate. To reduce the algal population, copper sulfate in a concentration of 1:500,000 is often added to the water without adverse affects on the aquatic fauna.

Certain algae and/or their products are toxic to animals. The so-called red tides which arise as a result of blooming of a dinoflagellate, *Gonyaulax cantenella,* result in an accumulation of toxins in shellfish which then cause illness and death if eaten. Toxins liberated during red tides also kill large numbers of fish. Other dinoflagellates, like species of *Gymnodinium* secrete toxic products. Blue-green algae—among others, *Microcystis aeruginosa* and its products or associated bacteria—have been indicted as agents causing poisoning of livestock.

Blue-green algae such as *Microcystis, Anabaena,* and *Aphanizomenon* have been implicated as causative agents in pain, nausea, vomiting and diarrhea, while other algae cause allergic manifestations and dermatitis in swimmers. Finally, in this connection, there has been educed some evidence that airborne algae may be associated with certain hitherto undiagnosed allergic conditions.

Algae in Biological Research

All the attributes of algae cited in earlier paragraphs of this chapter have been those which are adversely or favorably related to animals and man. It remains now to summarize briefly some aspects of the algae as they contribute to basic biological research.

Our advancing knowledge of the chemistry of photosynthesis and of other aspects of metabolism is based largely on studies of unicellular algae such as *Chlorella.* This is because of the relative ease and convenience of maintaining large uniform populations in a small space under rigidly controlled conditions.

Such organisms, furthermore, have been used in pilot studies as producers of oxygen and as beneficial agents in waste-disposal problems in spacecrafts.

Important studies on morphogenesis, nuclear function, nuclear–cytoplasmic relationships and ionic exchange with the environment have been conducted with great success on some large-celled algae such as *Acetabularia, Valonia* and *Nitella.* The large size of the protoplasmic unit (cell?) in these genera makes them especially favorable systems for experimentation.

The basic biological phenomenon of sexuality, its control and initiation, and mating-type compatibility are under intensive investigation in such favorable organisms as *Chlamydomonas* and *Oedogonium* (page 21). Such organisms may be grown readily in axenic culture under controlled conditions, and thus are suitable systems for study of basic sexual phenomena.

Although not as widely exploited as *Neurospora, Sordaria, Schizophyllum,* and other fungi, *Chlamydomonas* and certain of the desmids are being used in genetical studies. It is of interest, in this connection, that *Chlamydomonas* was the first *haploid* organism in which successful hybridization was accomplished (1916). An increasing number of morphological and biochemical mutants of *Chlamydomonas* have become available through the use of mutagens, and chromosome mapping for several species of the genus is progressing. It has also been demonstrated clearly that the cytoplasm in this organism has an important role in transmitting genetic information, in nonchromosomal inheritance, for example, resistance to streptomycin.

Finally, in the absence of simple chemical assays for such vitamins as B-12, certain algae (species of *Euglena* and *Chlamydomonas chlamydogama*) have proven useful as assay organisms.

CHAPTER

8

Introduction to the Fungi

THE **fungi** (singular, **fungus**) are plantlike, spore-bearing organisms which lack chlorophyll and are unable to synthesize their food. Consequently, they depend on other organisms for their nutrition. Fungi live as saprobes which bring about the decay of organic materials, or as parasites which attack living protoplasm and in so doing cause diseases of plants, animals, and humans.

A treatise such as this one entitled *Algae and Fungi* implies that these two groups are closely related. This belief has been widespread among botanists for many years. Structural resemblances, some of them superficial, between some fungi and some algae gave rise to the theory that the fungi originated from the algae by loss of chlorophyll. Present-day **mycologists,** specialists in the study of fungi (**mycology**), however, are not convinced that this theory has any factual basis. On the contrary, the most popular current theory is that the fungi may have originated from a protozoan ancestor and may not, therefore, be related to green plants in any way. In the present state of our knowledge, there is, of course, no valid reason to assume that all fungi originated from a common ancestor. Although this idea is appealing and phylogenetic fungal diagrams have been constructed to show how such evolution may have given rise to present-day forms from a single ancestor, it may very well be, as many mycologists now believe, that all fungi are not related. Some may have originated from a protozoan ancestor and others from a plantlike ancestor, perhaps some primitive alga which assumed a parasitic way of life and eventually lost its chlorophyll. Experimental investigations with algae, fungi, and protozoa may some day give us the answer to the origin and evolution of fungi. At present, discussing the fungi and the algae together, as we are doing here, is purely traditional and convenient.

What organisms should be included in the fungi is a matter of opinion. In its very broad definition—seldom used any more—the group encompasses the bacteria, the slime molds, and the so-called true fungi. The bacteria differ from the other two groups in that they possess primitive rather than highly organized nuclei which are found among the slime molds and the fungi. The bacterial nucleus, in common with that of the blue-green algae, is not surrounded by a nuclear membrane and does not possess a distinct nucleolus. The nuclei of the slime molds and the fungi, on the other hand, differ in no essential features from those of green plants and of animals. The bacteria are the subject of a separate book in this series and will, therefore, not be discussed here. The slime molds differ from the bacteria and from most fungi, in their naked, amoeboid assimilative stages and in their holozoic mode of nutrition. They resemble the true fungi in producing walled spores, usually borne in characteristic fruiting bodies. Traditionally the slime molds are studied by the mycologists but they show at least as strong affinities with the protozoa as they do with the fungi.

CHAPTER

9

The Slime Molds

THE NAME slime mold is applied to at least four distinct types of fungus-like organisms which differ in structure and physiology, and which have characteristic life histories. These are: the **cellular slime molds** (Acrasiales), the **net slime molds** (Labyrinthulales), the **plasmodial slime molds** (Myxomycetes), and the so-called **endoparasitic slime molds** (Plasmodiophoromycetes) which are probably true fungi. Whether these four groups are interrelated is not clear. Only two will be discussed here.

The Cellular Slime Molds (Order Acrasiales)

The Acrasiales are soil organisms. They are widespread geographically, and may be isolated by special methods from almost any type of soil. Their spore-bearing bodies are ephemeral and delicate. Thus they are never seen in the field and are known only from laboratory culture in which they develop profusely under proper conditions. If a soil suspension in which spores of the Acrasiales are present is plated-out together with bacteria on a weak hay-infusion agar, the spores will germinate and give rise to amoebae which feed on the bacteria, grow, and divide (Figure 9·1B–D). After several divisions a large amoebal population results. When the food supply is exhausted, some of these amoebae undergo certain changes, not as yet fully understood, and begin secreting **acrasin,** a hormone-like substance which attracts other amoebae causing them to stream toward a center of aggregation. These amoebae in turn secrete more acrasin attracting still more amoebae. Several such streams of amoebae are set up, all migrating toward a common point (Figure 9·1E). When a considerable number of amoebae has thus aggregated, a **pseudoplasmodium** (plural, **pseudoplasmodia**) is formed (Figure 9·1F). This is commonly called a "slug." The interesting feature of the slug is that although it behaves as a unit and responds to external conditions as though it were a single entity, it actually consists of a community or federation of thousands of amoebae, each of which retains its individuality. If we place a slug in wate: or if we agitate it

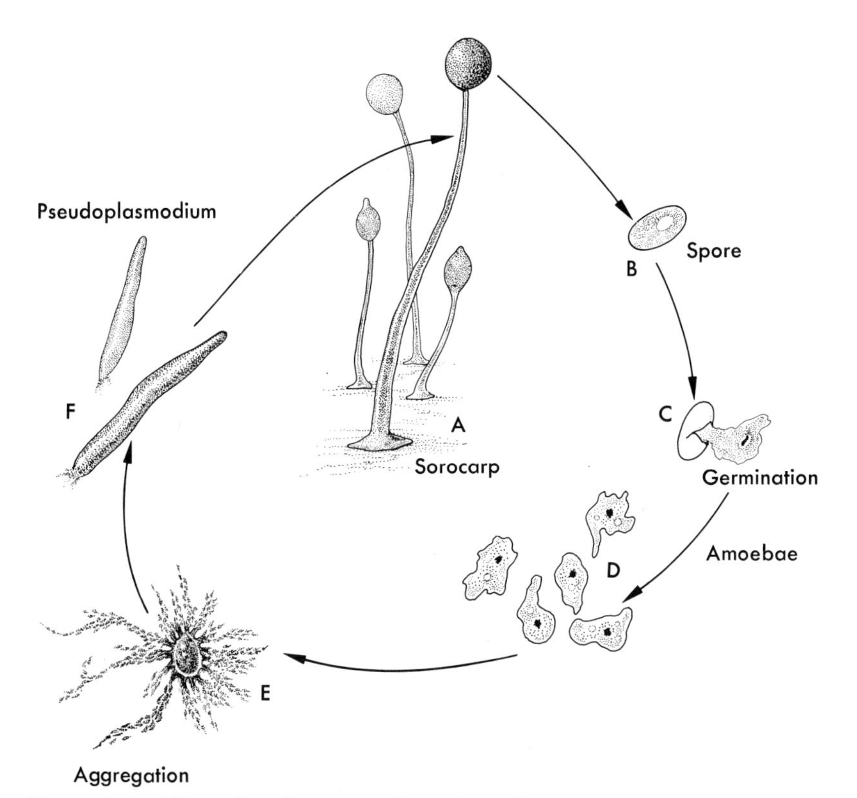

Figure 9·1. Life cycle of *Dictyostelium discoideum*. [From C. J. Alexopoulos, *Introductory Mycology*, 2d ed., New York: Wiley, 1962, p. 48.]

vigorously, we can break it into its component amoebae without in any way injuring the amoebae or impairing their ability to reaggregate. The amoebae of this community, at a certain point of organization, become physiologically differentiated in preparation for sporulation.

The slug at this stage raises itself upward, with its posterior end flattened against the substratum and its anterior end forming a nipple-like structure at the tip. The amoebae at the top then begin to migrate downward through the center of the slug, secreting cellulose walls and forming a cylinder downward toward the base. Thus the anterior amoebae are sacrificed in the formation of a cellular stalk which will eventually bear the spores. When the cellulose cylinder reaches the base, the amoebae at the base begin to migrate up the stalk and eventually form a mass at the tip (Figure 9·1A). There they are enveloped in thin, cellulose walls and become mature spores, held together by a droplet of viscous liquid.

Several kinds of cellular slime molds are known. These can be easily recognized by the morphology of their sporophores as shown in Figure 9·2.

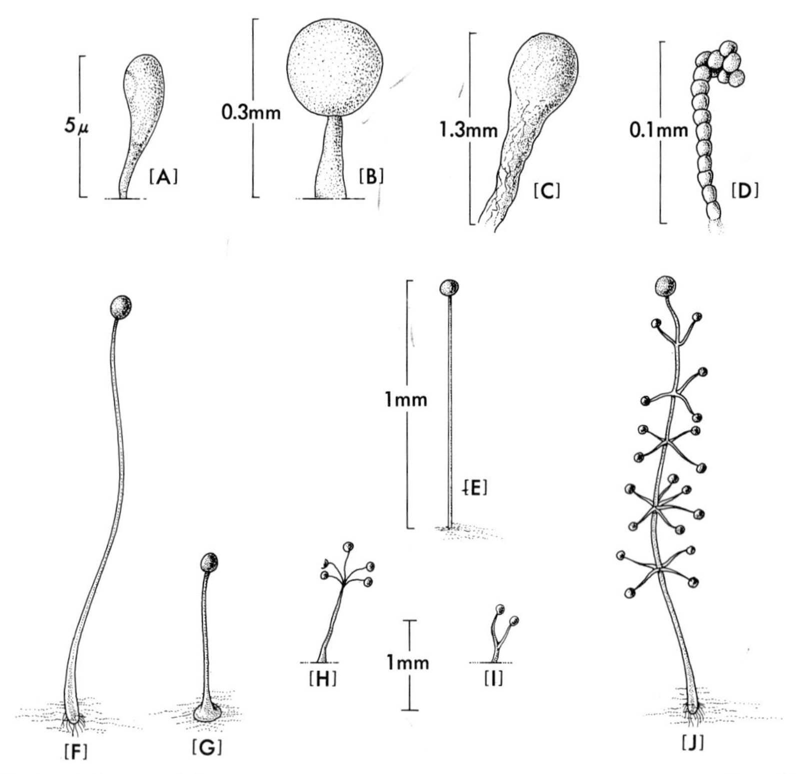

Figure 9·2. Acrasiales. Various types of sorocarps. **A:** *Sappinia.* **B:** *Guttulina.* **C:** *Guttulinopsis.* **D:** *Acrasis.* **E:** *Acytostelium.* **F–I:** *Dictyostelium.* **J:** *Polysphondylium.* [From C. J. Alexopoulos, *Introductory Mycology,* 2d ed., New York: Wiley, 1962, page 46.]

Much remains to be worked out concerning the activities of the cellular slime molds. One of the most controversial aspects of their life histories is the question of whether sexual reproduction takes place and, if so, at what point in the life cycle and in what manner?

Although the activities of the cellular slime molds appear to be of no direct importance to man, their value as experimental organisms in the study of the basic causes of morphogenesis has been considerable. *Dictyostelium discoideum* is being used in a number of biological laboratories for such studies.

The Plasmodial Slime Molds (Class Myxomycetes)

Biologists have studied the plasmodial slime molds (Myxomycetes) for many years in the field and have described about 400 different species the world over. Most of these are cosmopolitan and may be found wherever the conditions of temperature and moisture, in particular, are favorable for their development.

In contrast to the Acrasiales, the Myxomycetes are easily detected in the field and may be collected in one or the other of the two major phases of their life cycles: the **plasmodium** and the sporophores. The plasmodium (Figure 9·3), a free-living, multinucleate, naked, creeping mass of protoplasm devoid of cell walls but enveloped by a slimy sheath of unknown chemical composition, lives in moist dark areas, under the bark of decaying logs or under the moist leaves on the forest floor; it engulfs bacteria, various spores, and perhaps bits of decaying organic matter, feeding in an animal-like (holozoic) fashion. Eventually, the plasmodium emerges and in a matter of hours becomes converted into one large sporophore or, dozens of small, intricately

Figure 9·3. Plasmodium of *Physarum gyrosum* in agar culture. [Photo by C. J. Alexopoulos.]

constructed and often brilliantly colored fruiting bodies which bear the spores (Figure 9·4). In the majority of species the sporophore is about 1–2 mm tall. It consists of a walled sporangium often covered with lime, which may or may not have a stalk. Inside the sporangium are

Figure 9·4. Fruiting bodies of four species of Myxomycetes. A: *Diachea leucopodia* (×33). **B:** *Physarum viride* (×33). **C:** *Hemitrichia serpula* after external wall has disintegrated (×3). **D:** *Lycogala epidendrum* (×5). [Photos by C. J. Alexopoulos.]

thousands of spores, typically held together by a network of threads, the **capillitium** (plural, **capillitia**) (Figure 9·5). Spores and capillitium are independently formed at about the same time. In many species the capillitium is elastic. It expands when the sporangial wall bursts and carries with it the spore mass thus aiding in spore dissemination. In other species the capillitium may consist of a system of detached short threads which, because of their hygroscopic nature, twist and turn with changes in the humidity of the air, and thereby release the spores from the sporangia. In still other species the capillitium is not active in the dissemination of the spores but its intricate system of threads which tends to hold the spore mass together allows for the gradual dispersal of spores over a period of time. This is obviously advantageous to the slime mold for some spores are bound to be disseminated at times when conditions are favorable for their germination. Nevertheless, myxomycete spores are said to remain viable under unfavorable conditions for a very long time, as long as 60 or more years, according to some researchers.

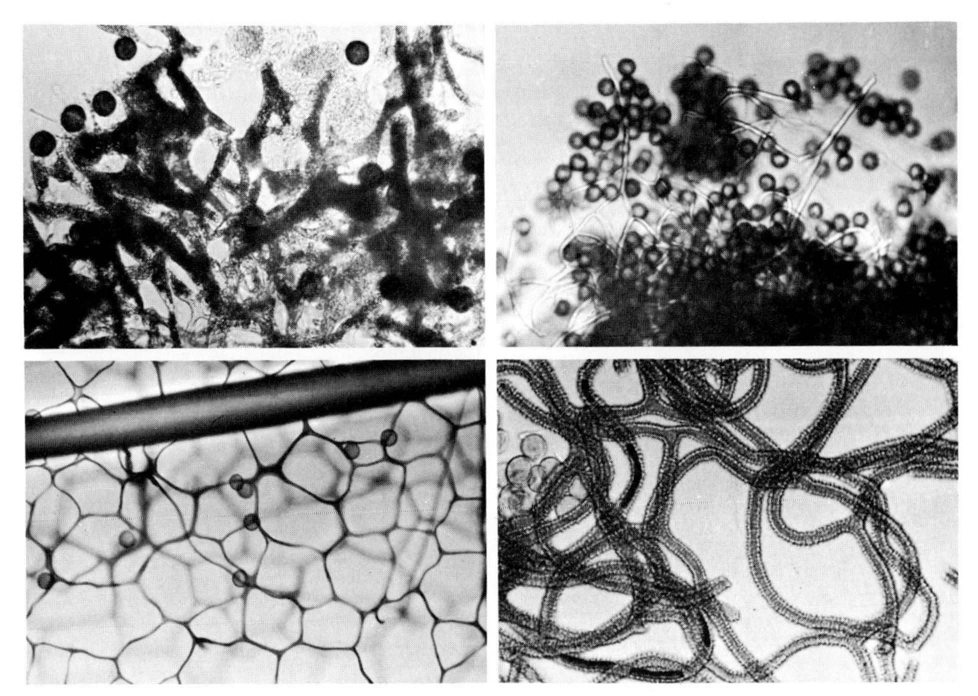

Figure 9·5. Four types of capillitium. All at the same magnification. [Photos by C. J. Alexopoulos.]

LIFE CYCLE

The life cycle of the Myxomycetes is illustrated in Figure 9·6. In the presence of water the spores germinate, each liberating one or more amoeboid swarm cells, each of which bears two unequal, anteriorly attached whiplash flagella. Swarm cells may fuse in pairs and form zygotes or they may first withdraw their flagella and become **myxamoebae** (singular, **myxamoeba**). If food (bacteria) is abundant the myxamoebae divide, forming large populations and then copulate in pairs forming zygotes.

In **homothallic** species all the gametes (myxamoebae or swarm cells) are compatible among themselves and, presumably, any two may fuse. In **heterothallic** species only gametes of different mating types are compatible. Gametes of different mating types are indistinguishable morphologically, but there is evidence that in some species they contain different amounts of DNA. The incompatibility mechanism in heterothallic Myxomycetes appears to be governed genetically by multiple alleles at a single mating-type locus. All alleles are compatible, at least in the few heterothallic species which have been investigated, but only gametes with different alleles fuse.

Whether a zygote is formed by the fusion of two compatible swarm cells or two compatible myxamoebae the end result is the same. The zygote feeds on bacteria and grows. Its nucleus soon divides mitotically and the binucleate structure thus formed is the first stage of the young plasmodium. From this point on the nuclei divide synchronously converting the binucleate structures into a multinucleate protoplasmic mass.

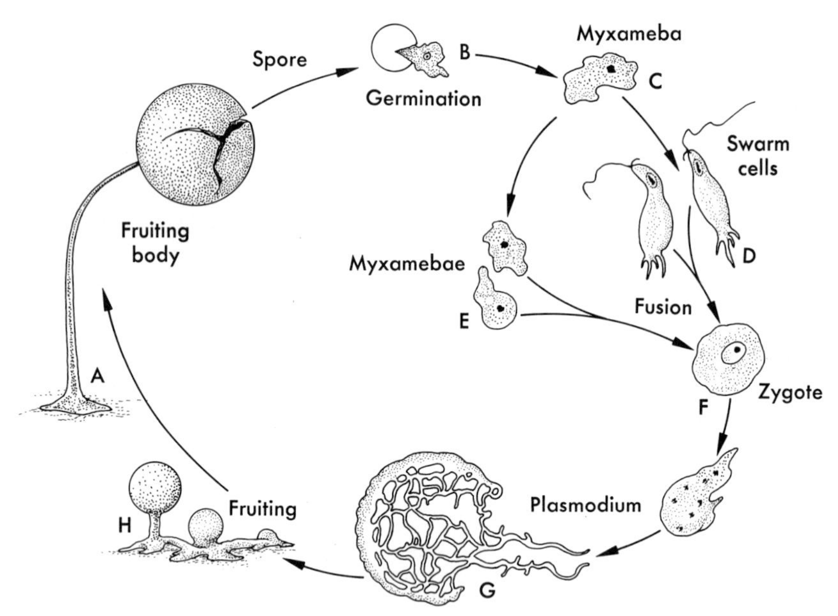

Figure 9·6. Life cycle of Myxomycetes. [From *A teachers guide for use with a series of three high school–college films on slime molds,* Audiovisual Center, University of Iowa.]

As the plasmodium moves over the substratum feeding on bacteria and other material, it grows by nuclear division and synthesizes new protoplasm. When two plasmodia of the same genetic makeup come into contact, the membranes break down and the cytoplasms of the two fuse into one matrix. The nuclei, already diploid, do not of course fuse. Contrary to what happens in many other organisms which have been investigated, DNA synthesis in the myxomycete plasmodium begins immediately after mitosis and reaches its peak rapidly. RNA synthesis appears to take place at a more or less constant rate throughout the intermitotic period. Under controlled experimental conditions in a synthetic liquid medium, in darkness at 23° C, the plasmodial nuclei of *Physarum polycephalum,* a well-known myxomycete, divide every 12 to 15 hours. Although all the nuclei in a given plasmodium divide synchronously, nuclei of different plasmodia in the same culture do not divide at the same time. When two plasmodia with different mitotic rhythms are permitted to fuse, mitotic synchrony is established in the new plasmodium within about 7 hours, indicating there is some regulatory mechanism which transmits information through the cytoplasm.

When a plasmodium has grown to a certain stage it usually develops an anterior fan-shaped region consisting of a sheet of protoplasm, often fleshy, which becomes reticulated just behind the forward zone and forms a network of vein-like strands. Observation through the microscope reveals that in most species of Myxomycetes each strand is a cylinder of jellified protoplasm enclosing a flowing protoplasmic stream. Slime mold plasmodia exhibit the most rapid protoplasmic streaming known in any organism. The stream flows in one direction, taking with it nuclei, vacuoles, pigment granules, and other inclusions, for about 40 to 60 seconds; it then slows down, stops momentarily, and reverses its direction of flow. This rhythmically reversible streaming in a plasmodium is a well-known and much studied phenomenon. The source of the motive force is not fully understood however. The best explanation we have at present is that the motive force is generated by an interaction of ATP and at least two contractile proteins (myxomyosin and myosin B) which have been found in the plasmodium of *Physarum polycephalum* and which are similar to actomyosin found in animal muscle. If this explanation is correct, the system in a slime mold plasmodium bears striking resemblance to the mechanism operating in animal muscle. Recent research with the electron microscope has also revealed the presence in the plasmodial cytoplasm of fibrils whose function some biologists believe to be related to protoplasmic streaming.

What chemical changes take place in a plasmodium at the time of fruiting and what triggers such changes are still matters of conjecture. Present indications are that a shift from cytochrome oxidases to ascorbic acid oxidases takes place at the time of fruiting. We do know that under experimental conditions pigmented plasmodia (and perhaps some which appear to lack pigments) require a certain period of illumination with wavelengths of 310–500 mμ. Niacin, nicotinamide, or certain substitutes also appear to be necessary for sporulation; the nutritional requirements for growth are different from those for fruiting. At the time fruiting is initiated, the plasmodium clumps and begins to form dome-shaped or column-like structures, each of which differentiates into a sporophore. The protoplast in the differentiating sporangium cleaves into a large number of uninucleate portions, each of which develops a wall and becomes a spore. Whether meiosis takes place just before cleavage or after the spores have become differentiated is a controversial question. It is probable that all species are not uniform in this respect. It appears, however, that regardless of when meiosis takes place, the fully mature spores are typically haploid.

Myxomycetes appear to be of little economic importance. However, we are just beginning to investigate their physiology and when we learn more about them we may discover that they play a greater role in nature than is presently believed. There are some indications, for example, that at least some species may be cellulolytic. We know also that myxomycete spores are present in the air in what may be significant numbers and that certain people show a definite skin reaction to proteins extracted from the spores.

Biochemists, biophysicists, and geneticists are using the Myxomycetes as tools in investigating properties of protoplasm, mitotic rhythms, DNA synthesis, inheritance mechanisms, and other fundamental biological processes. The fact that Myxomycetes can provide large quantities of relatively pure protoplasm is a distinct advantage in laboratory investigations of this nature. Heterothallic Myxomycetes, of which haploid and diploid phases can be maintained indefinitely in culture, are becoming especially important in studying the effects of ploidy on the physiology of an organism.

Although the myxamoebae and the plasmodia of several species of Myxomycetes have been grown in pure culture, no species has been induced to complete its entire life cycle in media of defined chemical composition in the absence of living or killed bacterial cells. This is the greatest stumbling block in morphogenetic studies at present and should be the object of intensive research in the immediate future.

CHAPTER

10

The True Fungi

THE FRUITING BODIES of many fungi are familiar to all. Mushrooms, puffballs, earthstars, and stinkhorns are commonly encountered in the woods, on lawns, in the golf course and even on the beaches. We are all aware of the activities of fungi. Farmers and gardeners know they must combat powdery mildews and downy mildews, leaf spots and blights, root rots and cankers, rusts and smuts if they wish to grow healthy plants. The baker and the brewer would be out of business without yeast. Roquefort and similar cheeses marketed as "blue cheese," owe their special flavor to a fungus. The most famous of all antibiotics, penicillin, is the product of another fungus. Together with the bacteria, fungi are responsible for the decay of dead plant and animal bodies and the return to the soil or atmosphere of such important elements as carbon, nitrogen, oxygen, and phosphorus.

The Fungal Thallus

GENERAL STRUCTURE

Although most people have seen the sporophores of the larger fungi, such as the mushrooms, few realize that these are only the spore-bearing structures and that they represent but a small part of the fungal life cycle. The soma or thallus of a fungus, the part that grows and obtains food and eventually produces the sporophore, is usually extensive but inconspicuous. It is composed of microscopic tubular filaments, the **hyphae** (singular, **hypha**) (Figure 10·1) which branch and rebranch

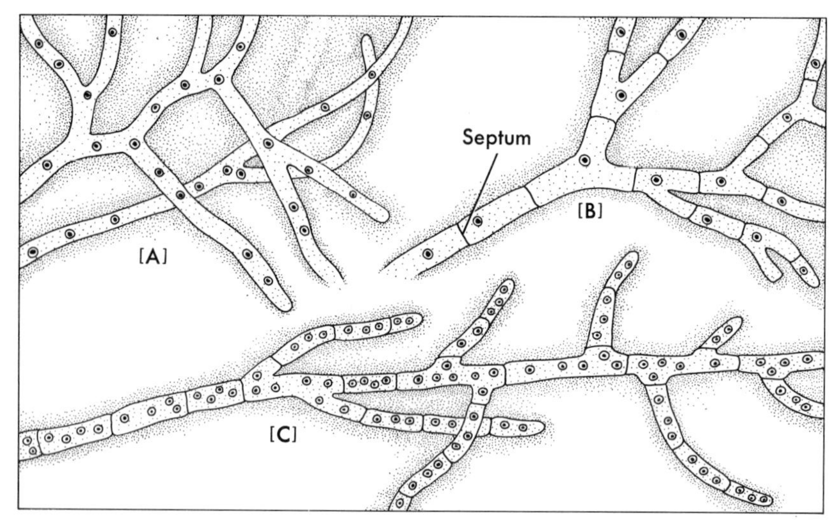

Figure 10·1. Three types of hyphae. A: Non-septate (coenocytic). **B:** Septate with uninucleate cells. **C:** Septate with multinucleate cells.

and spread in the substratum from which the fungus obtains nourishment. This system of hyphae we call the **mycelium** (plural, **mycelia**). The mycelium and the spores are, therefore, the two phases of a fungus which must always be kept in mind. The mycelium produces the spores and the spores produce the mycelium. There are many types of mycelia and even more of spores, and there is a very large number of ways in which the spores are produced, but the principle remains the same whether the fungal hyphae grow in a rotten orange and produce their spores on microscopic brushes or whether they grow in the soil at the edge of a forest and produce their spores in a giant puffball.

Not all fungi have mycelium. Some, like the common yeast, are unicellular. Others consist of a unicellular structure anchored on the substratum by a few rhizoids (Figure 10·2). Most fungi, however, are filamentous. The mycelium of filamentous fungi may be one continuous many-branched tube lined inside or filled with protoplasm, or it

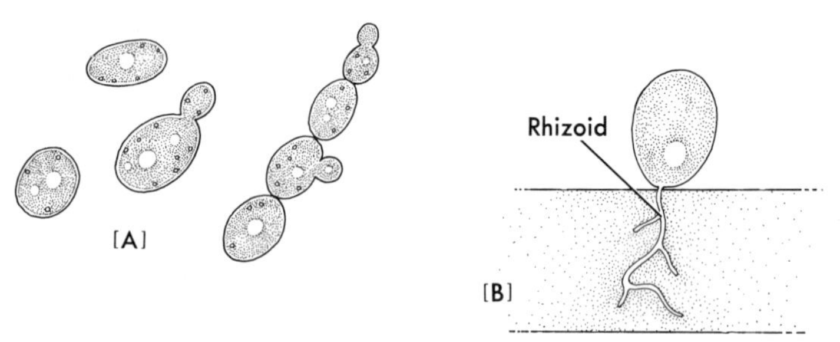

Figure 10·2. Unicellular fungi. A: Yeast cells showing formation of cell chains (pseudomycelium). **B:** A unicellular fungus with its rhizoid in the substratum.

may be divided into compartments (cells) by cross-walls called **septa** (singular, **septum**). Various types of septa will be described in connection with the fungi which possess them.

THE CELL WALL

Little is known of the physical structure of fungal cell walls but the use of modern techniques such as X-ray diffraction, electron microscopy, and biochemical analysis is beginning to yield valuable information. For example, it is now becoming apparent that fungal walls in general exhibit a fibrous structure and that they are composed of more than one layer. In the constant quest for criteria on which to base fungus relationships the chemical composition of the cell wall has been the subject of research for many years. Chemically, the fungal cell wall is a very complex structure. For a long time we have known that in some fungi the characteristic cell wall component is cellulose whereas in others it is chitosan or chitin. Recently it has been confirmed that in at least one fungus *(Rhizidiomyces)* both cellulose and chitin are present in the cell wall. It has also been claimed that this situation is more common than was formerly believed because chitin tends to mask the presence of cellulose. A discussion of chemical composition must also take into consideration that the chemistry of the cell wall changes with age and that among polymorphic fungi—in which the soma may be unicellular or filamentous, depending on the environment—the chemical composition of the cell wall may vary with the different phases.

The fungal wall is responsible for the rigidity of cells and hyphae, and we suspect that it plays an important role in various other cell activities, but the difficulties involved in localizing functions are so great that they impede rapid progress in research of this type. We know that many materials pass in and out of the cell through the cell wall but we have little knowledge concerning the role that the wall itself plays in this exchange. The difference in chemical composition of various morphological expressions of the same fungus may indicate that the cell wall indeed plays a part in morphogenesis. Studies with yeasts also indicate that clumping of cells accompanying sexual reproduction of the heterothallic *Hansenula wingei* is due to the interaction of a protein present on the cell wall of one mating type with a polysaccharide present on the wall of the opposite mating type. Thus the cell wall is probably not a passive covering of the fungal protoplasm, but an active component of the cell with important physiological functions.

STRUCTURE OF THE FUNGAL CELL

Relatively little has been published concerning the structure of the cytoplasm in the fungal cell, but in general it appears to conform to that of plant and animal cells; however, there are some differences. The presence of various types of membranes, vacuoles, mitochondria, Golgi apparatus, ribosomes, lipid inclusions, vesicles and most of the other major components of the cytoplasm of plant and animal cells has been amply demonstrated in at least some fungi. In addition it appears that certain other structures called lomasomes, observed in only a few other organisms to date, are characteristically present in fungal cells. Their function is unknown.

Cytoplasmic streaming in fungi appears in general to be unidirectional rather than rhythmically reversible as it is in the plasmodial strands of Myxomycetes. In fungal hyphae the cytoplasm streams toward the hyphal tip where growth takes place. This does not rule out the possibility that cytoplasm may also stream in reverse under certain conditions.

In **coenocytic** (non-septate) hyphae (Figure 10·1A), the nuclei are scattered throughout the cytoplasm. Septate hyphae are divided into compartments which may be uni-, bi-, or multinucleate (Figure 10·1B,C). In the so-called higher fungi, the septa are perforated and cytoplasmic strands connect adjacent cells. The difference, therefore, between a coenocytic and a septate hypha, rather than being absolute, is one of degree.

Fungi possess true nuclei with nuclear membranes and nucleoli. The nuclear membrane consists of at least two layers and has a large number of perforations over its entire surface. Ordinarily the nucleus appears as a spherical body but its shape is governed by its position in relation to other cell structures. For instance, when it is situated up against the cell wall it may appear hemispherical with one side flattened, or when it is in the process of passing through the pore of a septum it may appear dumb-bell shaped. The above statements imply that nuclei are motile. That they change position within a cell and that they migrate from cell to cell is undeniable, but the mechanics of movement are still very much obscure. It is presently thought that cytoplasmic streaming is responsible to a great extent for the movement of fungal nuclei and that the latter have no independent means of locomotion. Nevertheless, certain phenomena of orderly nuclear distribution in the hyphae of some fungi cannot adequately be explained on the basis of cytoplasmic streaming alone.

NUCLEAR DIVISION

Most studies of nuclear division in the fungi have concentrated on meiosis and, at present, not enough is known about the division of nuclei in the somatic cells to enable us to draw definite conclusions. A few papers that have been published claim that in certain yeasts and in some filamentous fungi, nuclei in somatic cells may undergo direct division rather than classical mitosis. In other fungi mitotic figures have been definitely demonstrated.

What can be said of meiosis is that "there appears to be no essential difference between the fungi and most other organisms in the basic cytological features and genetic implications of the meiotic process." [1]

GROWTH

The mycelium is initiated when a spore germinates. The spore absorbs water through its wall; the protoplast is activated; the nucleus divides; more protoplasm is synthesized; a bulge appears on the spore; more wall material is laid down; the bulge elongates into a tube; the nuclei divide successively, and the first hypha develops. All growth is apical thereafter. Some fungi grow so rapidly that hyphal growth may actually be observed under the microscope.

Optimum conditions for growth differ with different fungi. As a general rule, acid substrata and temperatures about 20–25° C favor growth of most fungi. Some species, however, are thermophilic and grow only at much higher temperatures. Fungal growth is inhibited but not prevented at low temperatures as any housewife, who has found moldy food in her refrigerator, knows. Aquatic fungi may be fresh-water or marine. The former do not tolerate high degrees of salinity but some can live in slightly brackish waters. Most aquatic fungi may be cultivated on solid media in the laboratory, but the majority of these will not sporulate under such conditions. They may be induced to sporulate, however, by providing them with an aquatic environment.

Fungi obtain food by secreting extracellular enzymes which digest portions of the substratum in which the hyphae grow. The digested material is then absorbed in solution directly through the walls of the hyphae. Some fungi have special rhizoids which absorb food. Parasitic fungi often produce special hyphal branches, the **haustoria** (singular, **haustorium**) which penetrate the cells of the host and obtain food from the protoplasm (Figure 10·3). The food then passes from the haustoria to the main hyphae which grow between the cells of the host.

Many fungi may be cultivated in axenic culture in the laboratory on synthetic media which contain the essential minerals and food substances from which the mycelium can manufacture proteins. The following elements appear to be necessary for the growth of fungi: C, H, O, N, P, K, S, Zn, Fe, Mg, Mn, Mo, Cu, and probably Ca. These must

---

[1] L. S. Olive, in G. C. Ainsworth and A. S. Sussman (eds.), *The Fungi,* Vol. I (see Selected References).

be supplied in a form that the fungus can utilize. C is usually supplied in the form of a sugar, such as glucose or maltose. Sucrose and soluble starch are utilized by many fungi also. N may best be supplied in the form of NH_4 salts or as amino acids. Many fungi, however, can utilize NO_3 salts. Each fungus has its own specific requirements which must be determined experimentally. Most fungi are able to synthesize the vitamins they need. However, many require thiamine or biotin or both and these two substances are usually added to synthetic media.

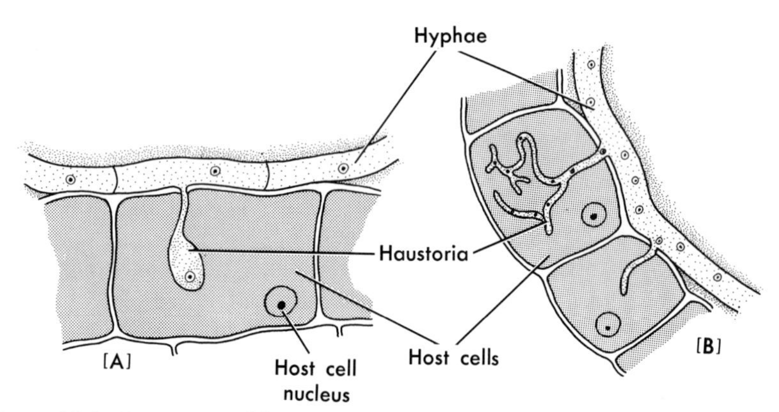

Figure 10·3. Two types of haustoria. A: Unbranched, bulbous type. **B:** Branched.

Although much is known concerning the nutritive requirements of fungi, even more remains to be discovered. We can grow the mycelial stages of many fungi in culture, for example, but we cannot induce sporulation. The well-known morel is a good example of this. On the other hand, we have learned enough about the requirements of some species so that we can prevent or induce sporulation at will.

NUTRITIONAL RELATIONSHIPS OF FUNGI TO OTHER ORGANISMS

In a previous section we pointed out that fungi are heterotrophic and must be supplied with the complex molecules already elaborated by green plants. We have also mentioned that in their mode of nutrition fungi are either saprobic or parasitic. There are, however, degrees of both of these conditions ranging from saprotism to obligate parasitism.

The majority of fungi are obligate saprobes. They cannot penetrate the defenses of a living organism and must obtain their nourishment from the dead bodies of plants and animals. Many fungi are **facultative parasites** (or facultative saprobes). They are capable of attacking living plants or animals thus causing disease, but they are also able to grow on nonliving organic material. Both obligate and facultative saprobes can be grown and studied in artificial culture in the laboratory. The most specialized group of fungi from the standpoint of nutrition are the **obligate parasites.** In nature, these live only on living protoplasm. They attack certain species of plants or animals and obtain their food from the living cells only. Some of these fungi are so virulent that they quickly kill the cells which they attack before their own hyphae have an opportunity to invade new living tissue; they perish as a result. These are the so-called super-parasites. We do not know enough about the physiology of obligate parasites to grow them on artificial media and must therefore study them on their living hosts. A **host** is a living organism which harbors a parasite.

The mycelium of most obligate parasites of plants enters the host through an opening such as a stoma, a lenticel, or a wound and grows within the tissues intercellularly. The hyphae obtain nourishment by means of haustoria which penetrate into the host cells. In spite of the fact that the presence of a haustorium in a host cell results in intimate contact between host and parasite, the haustorium does not actually penetrate the plasma membrane of the host cell but simply invaginates it. The two protoplasts thus appear to remain separated by the haustorial and the host membranes. Except in cases of attack by super-parasites, as mentioned above, the invaded host cells are not killed but continue to live and nourish the parasite for a long time.

Many different kinds of haustoria are known. Some are club-shaped, other are elongated and profusely branched. Special collars or other distinguishing features characterize the haustoria of certain species of fungi.

MYCORRHIZA. A number of facultative parasites form **mycorrhizae** (singular, **mycorrhiza**) with the roots of higher plants either by forming a mantle of fungal hyphae around the root, with some hyphae penetrating intercellularly, or by actually invading the root and living within the cells. It is generally accepted that both the fungus and the host benefit from this relationship but in many instances the fungus, always a parasite, gains the upper hand and destroys the rootlets it has invaded. In most instances the host plant keeps the fungus in check by various methods which are not too well understood. It has been shown experimentally that many plants do not grow nearly so well in the absence of the specific fungi which are normally present in the soil and form mycorrhizae. When the soil is inoculated with the proper fungi the plants grow normally.

In nature, the association of fungi and some plants appears to be an obligate one. Orchids, for example, never occur free of endophytic (growing inside) fungi. In the laboratory, however, orchids can be grown in pure culture (free from the fungi) if supplied with the nutrients they require which in nature they apparently obtain from the fungal hyphae.

THE LICHENS. Another interesting nutritional relationship between facultative fungal parasites and green plants results in the formation of lichens. A lichen is an association of a fungus with an alga. The relationship differs in its details in various specific combinations, but in general it may be said to be one of balanced parasitism in which most algal cells survive the attack of the fungus. The surviving algal cells are given a certain amount of protection (from intense light and dessication) by the fungal hyphae, which enables them to survive under circumstances which they might not be able to withstand alone. Thus lichens abound in certain habitats, such as the surface of exposed rocks, and localities, such as the arctic tundra and the antarctic, where few other plants thrive. In addition, however, they occur in places, such as the tropical rain forest where hundreds of plant species grow together and where the same algae that form lichens could probably be found living freely without a fungus associate.

The alga–fungus combination produces a plant body—the lichen thallus—which is characteristic of each specific association (Figure 10·4). Thus, lichens, in spite of their admittedly dual nature, are classified separately from the algae and fungi that compose them. The fungal element predominates in the lichen thallus and gives it its characteristic shape. The spores produced are those of the fungal associate. In laboratory cultures the spores germinate under favorable conditions and produce hyphae which, in the presence of a susceptible algal host, proceed to engulf and often to penetrate the cells of the latter and initiate a lichen thallus. It is probable that the same situation prevails in nature.

The thallus grows slowly and enlarges year after year, assuming its characteristic form. Lichens also propagate as such; portions of the thalli, composed of both algal and fungal elements, may break away and form new thalli.

By growing on otherwise bare rocks lichens, through both chemical and physical action, have been instrumental in the formation of soils over a long period of time. Lichens also are an important source of food for animals in localities where other food is scarce. Thus, in the winter, reindeer moss (a lichen), which is very common in northern regions, serves as the main food of reindeer.

PREDACIOUS FUNGI. A number of animal-trapping fungi have developed ingenious mechanisms for capturing small animals such as eelworms, rotifers, or protozoa which they use for food. Many of these animal traps are described in a very readable book by C. L. Duddington, *The Friendly Fungi.* Perhaps the most interesting of these mechanisms is that which utilizes a rapidly constricting ring around a nematode which holds it captive while the hyphae sink haustoria into the body of the victim. Several species of fungi in the genera *Arthrobotrys, Dactylella* and *Dactylaria* employ this method. In the presence of an eelworm population, the hyphae of the fungi produce loops which are stimulated to swell rapidly and close the opening when an eelworm passing through the loop rubs against its inner surface. It is thought that the amount of osmotically active material in the ring cells increases

Figure 10·4. Lichens. Note the large fruiting bodies (apothecia) in the lower photograph. [Photo courtesy of Vernon Ahmadjian.]

greatly as a result of stimulation and causes water to enter the cells increasing their turgor pressure. The ring cells swell rapidly and the ring closes around the eelworm which is thus held tightly in the trap (Figure 10·5). Whether this is the true explanation awaits the results of further experimentation.

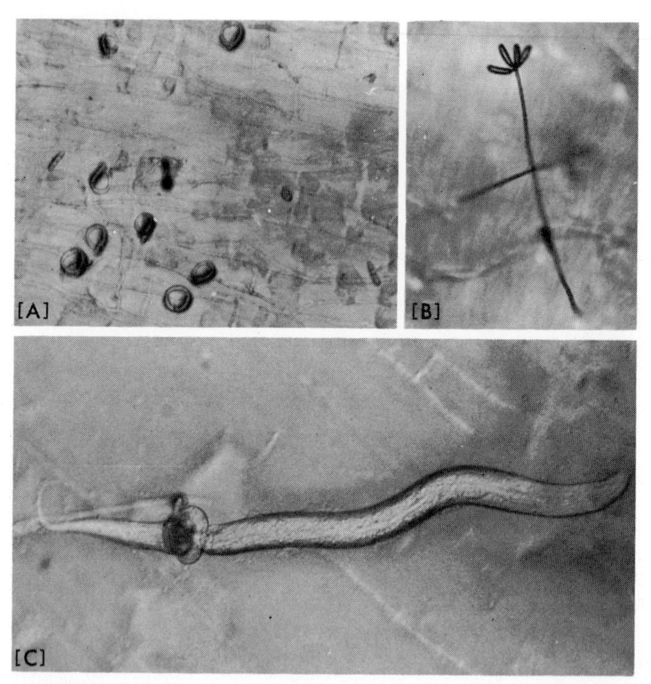

Figure 10·5. *Dactylaria*, a nematode-capturing fungus. A: Ring-like traps formed on the hyphae in response to the presence of nematodes in the culture. **B:** Conidiophore with conidia. **C:** Nematode held tightly by a constricted ring. [Photos by C. J. Alexopoulos.]

Some predacious fungi secrete a sticky substance on the surface of their hyphae to which a passing small animal adheres. Haustorium-like hyphae then grow into the body of the animal and absorb food. The animals so parasitized eventually die.

REPRODUCTION

Fungi reproduce both sexually and asexually. Sexual reproduction involves a fusion of nuclei. Asexual reproduction is simpler and more direct. Asexual reproduction in unicellular fungi, such as the yeasts, is accomplished by simple cell division or by budding. In the latter process, an outgrowth (bud) is produced by the mother cell (Figure 10·2A). The nucleus divides and one of the two daughter nuclei migrates into the bud which then grows and eventually becomes severed from the mother cell. Fragmentation is another common method of asexual reproduction. Any fragment of a vigorously growing mycelium is capable of growing into a new individual when placed under conditions favorable for growth. This method is commonly used in the laboratory for propagating fungi in culture.

The most important method of asexual reproduction in fungi is the production of spores. When the mycelium of a fungus reaches a certain stage of maturity it begins to produce spores if the conditions under which it is growing are favorable for sporulation. A great many fungi produce two types of spores. One type is produced asexually. The other type is the result of sexual reproduction. Asexually formed spores are usually produced first. Sexual reproduction generally occurs when the mycelium has attained a greater maturity. In nature, many phytopathogenic fungi (organisms which cause plant disease), go through several asexual generations throughout the growing season and do not reproduce sexually until the end of the summer. In such fungi, sexual reproduction results in a thick-walled spore or spore fruit which carries the fungus over the severe winter conditions and the life cycle is resumed the following spring. Asexually produced spores may be borne in sac-like structures, the **sporangia** (singular, **sporangium**) or directly on hyphae (Figure 10·6). Spores borne in sporangia are called **sporangiospores**; those borne directly on hyphae are **conidia** (singular,

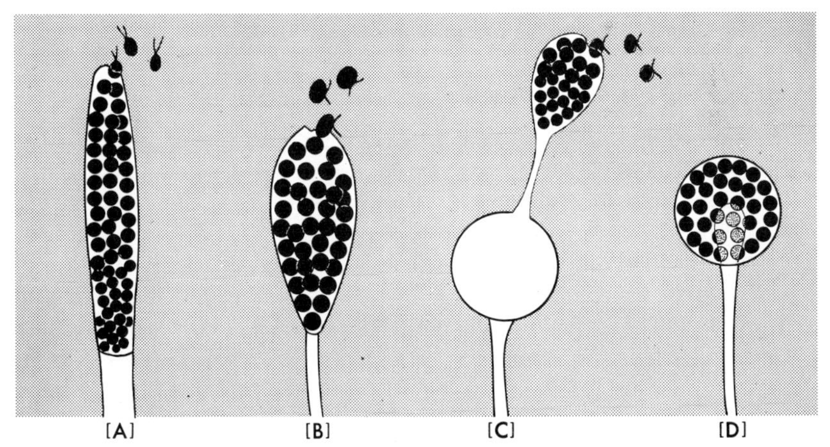

Figure 10·6. Four types of sporangia. **A:** Elongated, hypha-like. **B:** Oval. **C:** Globose sporangium releasing zoospores through a vesicle. **D:** Globose sporangium with columella.

conidium) (Figure 10·7). Conidia are never motile. Sporangiospores of some species, on the other hand, may be equipped with one or two flagella. They are then capable of swimming and are similar to the zoospores of algae. Sporangiospores which have no flagella are nonmotile and are called **aplanospores** by mycologists.

Sexual reproduction consists of three stages: plasmogamy, karyogamy, and meiosis. Plasmogamy is the mechanism which brings two compatible nuclei together in a single protoplast in preparation for nuclear fusion. It may be accomplished in various ways. Karyogamy is the actual fusion of the two nuclei following plasmogamy. Karyogamy results in a zygote nucleus which is diploid. Meiosis eventually takes place and restores the haploid condition. In most fungi, the soma (thallus) is haploid and the diploid condition is confined to but a single cell (the zygote); meiosis usually takes place soon after karyogamy. There are some notable exceptions to this rule however.

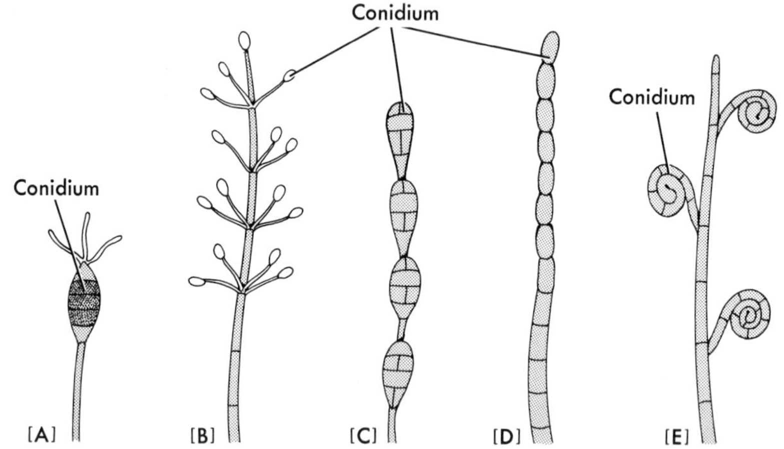

Figure 10·7. Various types of conidia. A: Multiseptate with transverse septa only and with appendages (setae). **B:** Oval, borne singly. **C:** Muriform (with both vertical and horizontal septa). **D:** Oval, borne in a chain. **E:** Helical.

In the so-called higher fungi, meiosis is followed by the production of 4 or 8 (rarely fewer or more) spores which are the direct products of the tetrad. This fact has been exploited by the geneticists who now use fungi (*Neurospora, Saccharomyces, Schizophyllum,* and others) extensively for genetic investigations. Spores produced as a direct result of meiosis are termed **meiospores.**

Fungi produce a large variety of spores. Every conceivable shape and size of spore may be found in the fungus world. This great diversity in spore morphology makes the fungi particularly interesting subjects for study. Perhaps the majority of fungi depend on wind or water for the dispersal of their spores, but many fungi have developed particularly interesting mechanisms for spore dissemination. We shall discuss some of these in a later section.

CHAPTER

11

The Kinds of Fungi

According to very conservative estimates there are over 50,000 species of fungi inhabiting the earth. Many are cosmopolitan. Others seem to be greatly restricted in their distribution.

In accordance with our present system of classification, all fungi are placed in the Division or Phylum Mycota which is included in the Plant Kingdom by some biologists, in the Kingdom Protista by others, or in a separate kingdom: The Fungi. The Division Mycota includes 9 classes in addition to the Myxomycetes which we have already discussed. These are: Chytridiomycetes, Hyphochytridiomycetes, Oomycetes, Plasmodiophoromycetes, Zygomycetes, Trichomycetes, Ascomycetes, Basidiomycetes, and Deuteromycetes. We shall discuss only a few of these.

Class Chytridiomycetes

The Chytridiomycetes are typically aquatic but some live in moist soil from which they are often isolated. Although they vary enormously in their general morphology all produce motile cells (zoospores or gametes), each equipped with a single, posterior, whiplash flagellum. The chief component of the cell walls in this class appears to be chitin.

Many Chytridiomycetes are parasitic on algae. Some parasitize small water animals. A few are parasitic on seed plants. Economically, the only one of any importance is *Synchytrium endobioticum* which causes a disease of potatoes called "black wart."

Perhaps the most interesting, although not the most typical, of these fungi is *Allomyces,* a water mold which is widely distributed throughout the world but which is particularly abundant in warmer climates. *Allomyces* has been studied carefully and its unique life history (Figure 11·1) is now well understood.

This fungus is of particular interest because it is the only filamentous fungus known which exhibits a true alternation of generations with a diploid filamentous **sporothallus,** which produces the spores, alternating with a haploid filamentous **gametothallus,** which produces the gametes.

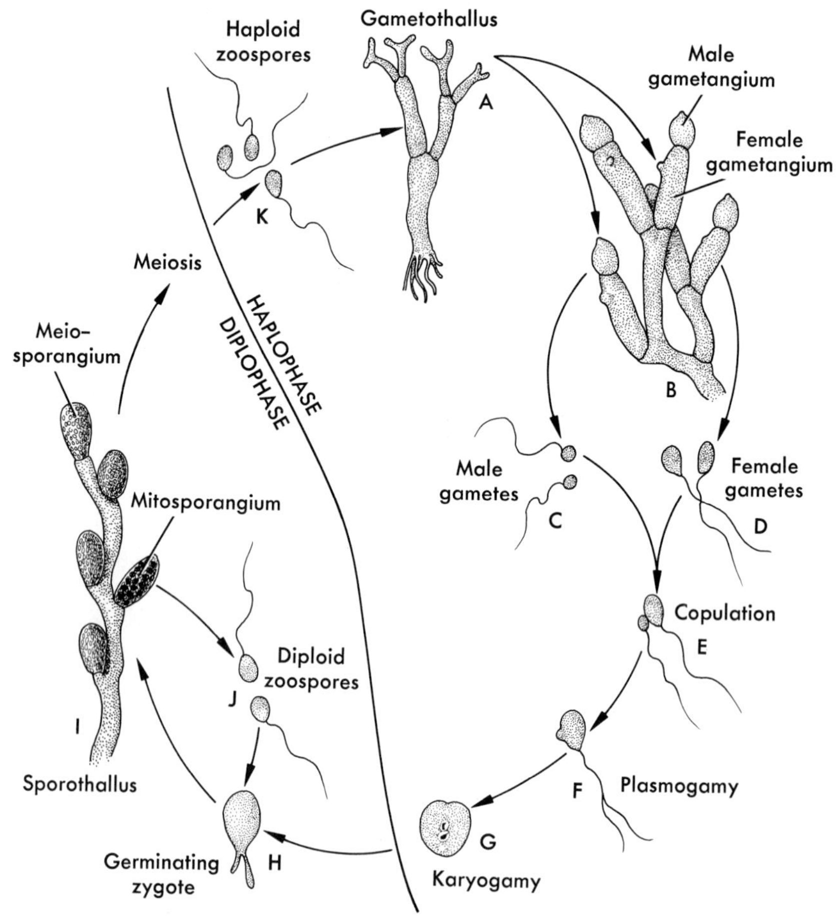

Figure 11·1. Life cycle of *Allomyces macrogynus*. [From C. J. Alexopoulos, *Introductory Mycology*, 2d ed., New York: Wiley, 1962, p. 120.]

The multinucleate thallus of *Allomyces* consists of well-developed rhizoids, which anchor the organism to its substratum, and a trunk which divides dichotomously forming branches which bear the reproductive organs. The thalli are typically nonseptate, but septa are produced at the base of the reproductive organs. Gametothalli and sporothalli are similar morphologically and can only be distinguished by the types of reproductive organs they eventually produce. At the tips of its branches a gametothallus bears large female gametangia and much smaller male gametangia (Figure 11·2A,B,C). The former contain a few large female gametes and the latter contain many small male gametes. The female gametes are colorless; the male contain carotenoid pigments and are, therefore, orange-colored. When the gametes mature, the gametangia develop small papillae which break and permit the release of the gametes into the water. The female gametes secrete a diffusable chemotactic substance, termed **sirenin,** effective at very low concentrations, which attracts the male gametes. Male and female gametes then fuse in pairs, and zygotes are formed. Each zygote swims for a time, comes to rest, encysts, germinates, and grows into a diploid sporothallus.

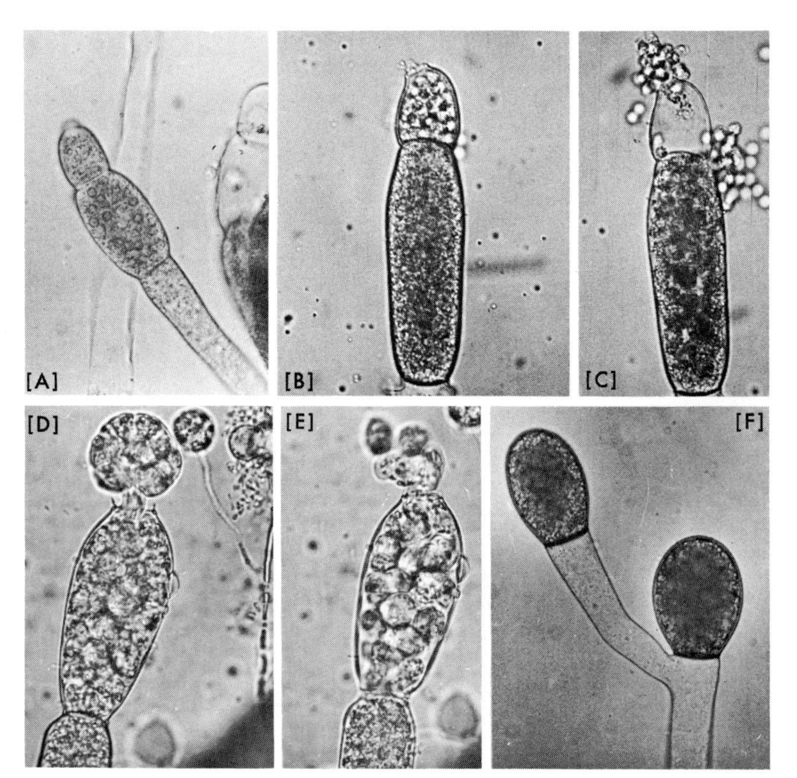

Figure 11·2. ***Allomyces macrogynus.*** **A:** Gametangia—male at tip, female below. **B:** Male gametes mature, female not yet differentiated. **C:** A few minutes later—male gametes are released, females are differentiated. **D:** Mitosporangium releasing a mass of mitospores. One mitospore released earlier from another mitosporangium has germinated. **E:** Same mitosporangium a few moments later. **F:** Two meiosporangia. [**D** and **E,** by H. C. Bold. Other photos by C. J. Alexopoulos.]

Sporothalli produce two types of sporangia: thin-walled, elongated **mitosporangia** (Figure 11·2D,E) and thick-walled, brown, pitted **meiosporangia** (Figure 11·2F). The mitosporangia release diploid zoospores each of which grows into a new sporothallus. The meiosporangia require several weeks of drying and rest before they germinate. At the time of germination, their nuclei undergo meiosis. Each haploid nucleus becomes incorporated in a motile, haploid meiospore. The meiosporangium then cracks open, releasing the meiospores, each of which grows into a new gametothallus.

Class Oomycetes

The Oomycetes constitute a fairly large and very important class of fungi. Some live in water, others in soil, and still others in association with terrestrial seed plants. Biologically they range from saprobes through facultative parasites to obligate parasites.

Among economically important Oomycetes are *Saprolegnia parasitica* which attacks fish and fish eggs in hatcheries; *Aphanomyces eutyches,* the cause of a serious disease in sugar beets and other plants; and various other fungi which cause downy mildews, blights, and white rusts of many important crop plants. *Phytophthora infestans,* the cause of late blight of potatoes, was responsible for the great Irish famine of 1845 during which thousands of people died of starvation and which was directly responsible for the repeal of the "corn laws" of Britain. The famine, a result of repeated crop failures caused by this fungus, brought about a wave of migration of the Irish people to the Western Hemisphere. Downy mildew of grapes, caused by another oomycete, *Plasmopara viticola,* would have destroyed the French wine industry except for the timely discovery of Bordeaux mixture, the first important fungicide, which finally controlled the disease.

The characteristic component of the cell walls of Oomycetes appears to be cellulose. Whether the thallus of the Oomycetes is haploid or diploid is a controversial subject. Cytological investigations in the early part of the century indicated that in some members of this class, meiosis occurs in the gametangia during the development of the gametes and that the nuclei of the thallus are therefore diploid. These conclusions were not generally accepted by mycologists, however, and subsequent authors have assumed that meiosis in the Oomycetes, as in most other fungi, occurs soon after karyogamy, making the zygote the only diploid structure in the life cycle. Very recent work indicates that the early investigators may have been correct and that the Oomycetes may be unique as a class among fungi in possessing a diploid thallus. This raises the question of their origins and their relationship to other fungi and furnishes a strong argument to those who support the theory of a polyphyletic origin and evolution of the fungi.

Oomycetes may be unicellular or filamentous. The mycelium of the filamentous Oomycetes typically consists of nonseptate hyphae which, however, produce septa at the base of the reproductive organs. Such septa are typically solid plates. The Oomycetes reproduce asexually by producing sporangia which in most species release zoospores. The zoospores are either pear-shaped or kidney-shaped. They are biflagellate, bearing one whiplash and one tinsel flagellum. The flagella of pear-shaped (primary) zoospores are attached anteriorly; those of kidney-shaped (secondary) zoospores are attached at the side in the depression of the zoospore. Sexual reproduction takes place oogamously by the transfer of nuclei from club-shaped antheridia to usually spherical oogonia containing one or more eggs. No motile gametes are produced. The water molds, cosmopolitan in their distribution and easy to isolate, serve as typical examples of this class of fungi.

To isolate water molds for study, go to the nearest pond or lake and obtain a quart of water. Divide it equally into two quart jars and bait it with three or four dead flies or some boiled pieces of corn kernels or other seeds. Boiled, split hemp seeds give the best results, but it requires a special permit to obtain these seeds because they are the source of marijuana and their use is restricted. In a few days the bait will have become the center of a water mold colony and the nonseptate tubular, multinucleate hyphae will radiate in the water in all directions. In all probability the fungus you have caught will be a member of either the genus *Achlya* or the genus *Saprolegnia,* the most common of the water molds.

The tips of many of the hyphae will soon develop into elongated sporangia which will release biflagellate zoospores. If the zoospores encyst and form spore balls at the mouth of the sporangium the fungus is an *Achlya* (Figure 11·3). The primary zoospores of *Saprolegnia* swim away individually and encyst after a considerable period of activity. The encysted spores eventually germinate, each releasing a secondary, kidney-shaped zoospore which will start a new fungal colony. As the mycelium ages and the food supply is depleted, sexual reproduction is initiated. Male and female sex organs, easily distinguished as antheridia and oogonia, are produced. Each oogonium usually contains from 1 to 20 or more spherical uninucleate eggs. The antheridia become appressed to the oogonia, and send copulation tubes into them toward the eggs. Male nuclei then migrate from the antheridia to the eggs and each egg nucleus fuses with one antheridial nucleus. The fertilized egg then becomes a thick-walled oospore and undergoes a rest period. When it eventually germinates, it produces a hypha which soon produces a sporangium. As mentioned earlier, the time of meiosis in the life cycle is not known. Until very recently meiosis was believed to take place at the time the oospore germinates but recent research indicates it may take place in the antheridia and oogonia preceding gamete formation. If this is true, then the entire thallus is diploid, the only haploid structures being the eggs and the antheridial nuclei.

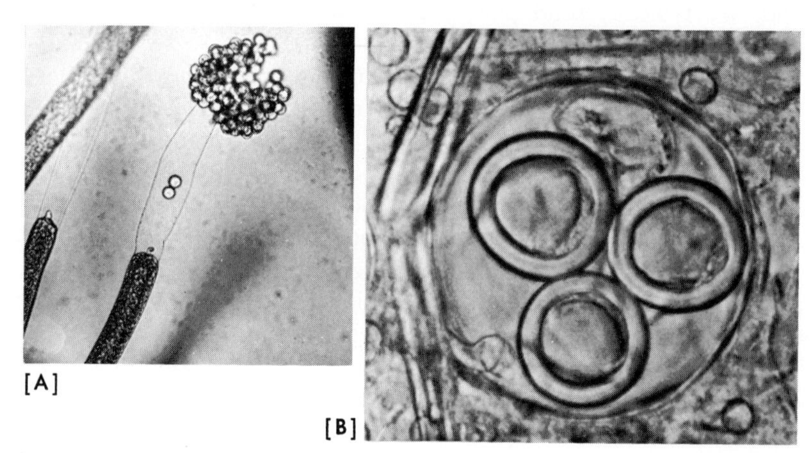

Figure 11·3. Reproduction in *Achlya*. A: A sporangium with a ball of encysted zoospores at its orifice. **B:** Oogonium, containing three oospores. [**A** from H. C. Bold, *Morphology of Plants,* New York: Harper & Row, 1957, p. 168; **B** by C. J. Alexopoulos.]

Most species of water molds are homothallic—that is, single individuals are capable of reproducing sexually without the aid of others. *Achlya ambisexuallis,* however, is morphologically heterothallic. In this species some individuals produce oogonia and others antheridia. Sexual reproduction in this species is governned by a complex system of sex hormones. When male and female thalli are present in close proximity, the two thalli secrete hormones which (1) activate the potentially male thallus to produce antheridial hyphae, (2) stimulate the female thallus to produce oogonial initials, (3) attract the antheridial hyphae toward the oogonia, (4) induce delimitation of the antheridia. Finally, there is the delimitation of the oogonia and the differentiation of the eggs.

Many Oomycetes, parasitic on plants, such as the aforementioned *Phytophthora infestans* and *Plasmopara viticola,* pass their entire life cycle inside the tissues of their plant hosts, producing their sporangia on the host surface. It is of particular interest that in spite of a non-aquatic habitat, the majority of such fungi continue to produce zoospores which require water for their activity. Sporangia of such fungi usually break away from the hyphae that bear them and are disseminated by wind. Falling upon the leaves or stems of susceptible plant hosts they release zoospores when the plants are wet and the temperature is favorable. The zoospores swim on the film of water for a while, encyst, and then germinate, each by a germ tube, which usually enters the host through a stoma or other opening. If conditions are not favorable for zoospore production, however, the sporangia themselves assume the function of spores and germinate directly by producing germ tubes. The resulting mycelium henceforth grows internally and eventually produces sporangia often on special hyphal branches, the **sporangiophores,** which emerge through the stomata or burst through the epidermis. Production of zoospores by terrestrial fungi is interpreted as an indication of descent from aquatic ancestors.

Class Zygomycetes

The Zygomycetes are terrestrial fungi. They differ from both Chytridiomycetes and Oomycetes in that (1) they produce no motile cells and (2) they reproduce sexually by the fusion of two, generally equal, gametangia which results in the formation of a **zygospore.**

The thallus of the Zygomycetes is filamentous. The hyphae are generally nonseptate, at least when young. Septa may be formed, however, as the mycelium ages. In some species the hyphae are septate from the beginning. The characteristic component of the hyphal wall is chitin, but cellulose may also be present along with it.

The Zygomycetes live in the soil, on dung, or on decaying plant and animal matter. Most are saprobic but some are parasitic. Among the latter are some weak parasites of plants. Others parasitize insects, small soil animals such as amoebae or nematodes, and a few attack the human body causing diseases known as Mucormycoses. Zygomycetes are employed in industry for the production of certain organic acids such as fumaric, oxalic, and lactic and some are used in the production of cortisone. *Rhizopus oryzae* is used extensively in fermentation processes, especially in the Orient where it is employed in making rice wine (sake) and other alcoholic preparations. The most familiar of these fungi is probably *Rhizopus stolonifer,* the common bread mold whose life cycle will be used as an example of this class of fungi (Figure 11·4).

The mycelium of *Rhizopus* consists of non-septate, multinucleate hyphae which grow rapidly and exhibit easily visible protoplasmic streaming. The aerial hyphae, called **stolons,** form a group of rhizoids when they come in contact with the substratum. Opposite the rhizoids one or more sporangiophores originate, each forming a more or less globose sporangium at its tip. The sporangium begins as a swelling into which a number of nuclei flow. These nuclei are mainly concentrated in the periphery of the developing sporangium. The central portion with few nuclei now becomes separated from the peripheral zone by the

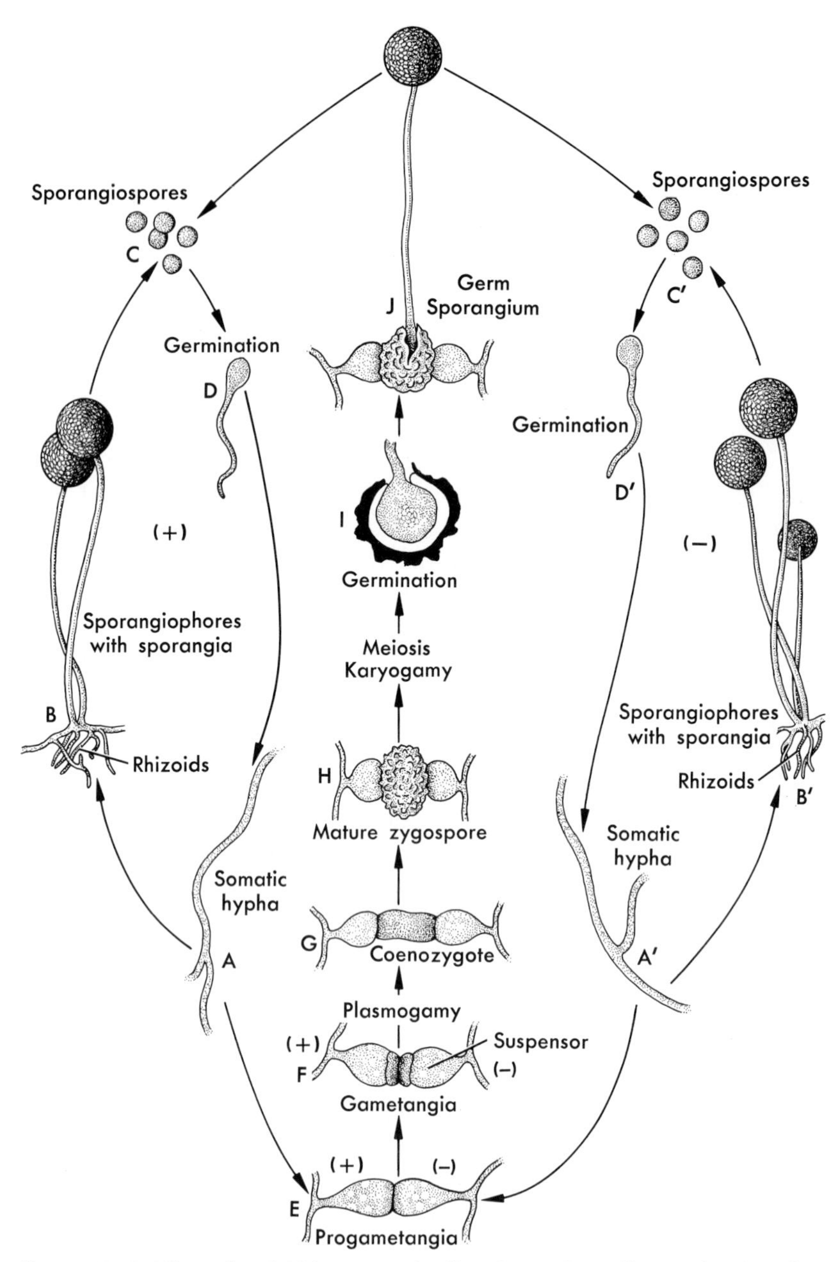

Figure 11·4. Life cycle of *Rhizopus stolonifer*. [From C. J. Alexopoulos, *Introductory Mycology*, 2d ed., New York: Wiley, 1962, p. 196.]

deposition of a wall, and becomes the **columella** (plural, **columellae**). The protoplasm surrounding it soon is cleaved into small portions which develop into sporangiospores. When the sporangium is mature, its wall breaks open and the spores are disseminated. Each spore is capable of germinating to form a hypha.

Rhizopus stolonifer is heterothallic. Sexual reproduction, therefore, requires the presence of two thalli of different mating types. The thalli are indistinguishable morphologically and are therefore designated as *plus* (+) and *minus* (−) instead of male and female. When both mating types are present a hormonal mechanism operates which causes the hyphal tips to differentiate into **progametangia** which come in contact and develop into gametangia by the formation of septa. The walls between two contiguous gametangia dissolve and the two multinucleate gametangial protoplasts coalesce. Plus and minus nuclei now approach each other and fuse in pairs, producing many zygote nuclei. The structure which contains them is the **coenozygote.** Soon the wall of the coenozygote thickens, turns black, and becomes rough. The whole structure, now termed the **zygospore,** enters a rest period which lasts from 1 to 3 or more months. At the time of germination meiosis takes place, the zygospore cracks open, and a single sporangiophore bearing a **germ sporangium** at its tip emerges. The germ sporangium is similar to an asexually produced sporangium. Some germ sporangia contain spores all of one mating type (+ or −) but others contain spores of both mating types in about equal numbers.

The sporangiospores of *Rhizopus* are wind disseminated as are those of many other species of Zygomycetes. Of particular interest in this connection is the spore dispersal mechanism of *Pilobolus,* the "hat thrower," a dung-inhabiting (coprophilous) fungus which discharges its entire sporangium violently by a jet propulsion mechanism. *Pilobolus* produces its spores in a sporangium, the upper wall of which is thickly cutinized. The sporangial apparatus is positively phototropic and the light sensitive region is situated so that the sporangium points toward the source of light. At the junction of sporangium and stalk, the wall is thin, creating a region of weakness. Chemical changes which occur in the sporangiophore result in an increase in osmotic pressure which creates great hydrostatic pressure within the sporangium, bursting the wall. The sporangial wall contracts, squirting a jet of liquid behind as the sporangium with all its spores is propelled several feet through the air. Because of an adhesive substance on its surface the sporangium adheres to any solid object it strikes. In nature this is likely to be a blade of grass or the stem of some herbaceous plant. Herbivorous animals grazing in the field eat the sporangia together with the grass. The spores are excreted with the dung. In a general way, sexual reproduction in *Pilobolus* is similar to that described for *Rhizopus.*

Another zygomycete which discharges its sporangium explosively is *Basidiobolus ranarum,* a fungus which grows on the excreta of frogs and lizards. Its life history is very interesting. The mycelium of *Basidiobolus* is septate and the cells are uninucleate. After it makes considerable growth it begins to produce at the tips of hyphal branches, small spherical units which look like spores but which are actually sporangia which have not as yet developed spores. These sporangia are violently discharged and are soon eaten by beetles which in turn are eaten by frogs or lizards. When the beetles are digested, the sporangia are set free in the frog's stomach. At that time, cleavage of the sporangial contents occurs, and sporangiospores are formed which are liberated in the frog's digestive tract. The spores multiply by budding and are eventually voided unharmed with the excreta to germinate on the dung and produce mycelium. Sexual reproduction results in the formation of zygospores. *Basidiobolus ranarum,* considered until recently to be only a saprobe, is now believed to be a causal organism of a human disease as well.

Class Ascomycetes

INTRODUCTION

The Ascomycetes (sac fungi) constitute an enormous and varied group of fungi many of which are exceedingly important in agriculture, in medicine, and in industry. A large number of serious plant diseases, some of them catastrophic, are caused by Ascomycetes. Apple scab, brown rot of stone fruits, various powdery mildews which attack grapes, peaches, roses, and gooseberries, are caused by Ascomycetes. *Endothia parasitica,* an ascomycete native to the Orient, accidentally introduced to the United States has completely destroyed the American chestnut. It has now invaded Europe and threatens the European chestnut with the same fate. *Ceratocystis ulmi,* another ascomycete, accidentally introduced from Europe into the United States is slowly but relentlessly exterminating the American elm. The fungus is carried by a bark beetle which can be controlled by spraying the trees with DDT. This chemical is lethal to birds and insects alike, however, and cities heavily planted with elms have faced the dilemma of whether to save the elms and kill the birds or save the birds and denude the streets. An interesting ascomycete is the ergot fungus *Claviceps purpurea.* Its mycelium attacks rye and other cereals and reduces the yield; its **sclerotia** (singular, **sclerotium**) (hard, resting bodies) contain poisonous alkaloids which are lethal to grazing animals and to man. Ergot is important in medicine for the control of hemorrhage, particularly during child birth. The sclerotia of *Claviceps purpurea* are the original source of LSD the much discussed hallucinogenic agent; its discovery and use in the treatment of mental illness are described by Lucy Kavaler in her interesting book *Mushrooms, Molds, and Miracles.*

Baker's or brewer's yeast—depending on one's point of view—is another ascomycete. The delectable and expensive truffle, a product of France, is yet another commercially important ascomycete. In the research laboratory the ascomycete *Neurospora* has been responsible for far-reaching discoveries in the study of heredity. *Neurospora* was discovered in 1927 by botanists Cornelius Shear and Bernard O. Dodge of the United States Department of Agriculture. In a series of brilliant, fundamental, pioneering researches Dodge showed how *Neurospora* could be used in genetic research. Geneticists and biochemists alerted by Dodge's discoveries developed the important field of biochemical genetics which elucidated the control of biochemical pathways in living organisms.

The one important character which distinguishes the Ascomycetes from all other fungi is the **ascus** (plural, **asci**). This is a sac-like structure in which **ascospores** are formed following karyogamy and meiosis.

The Ascomycetes produce no motile cells. Even though some of them live in aquatic habitats, no swimming spores or gametes are produced by any known species.

THE YEASTS

Yeasts are unicellular Ascomycetes. In nature they occur on the surface of fruits, in the nectar of flowers, in the slime flux exuding from trees, in the soil, and even in water. They have the ability to ferment sugars and in so doing produce alcohol and CO_2. Man has taken advantage of this property of yeasts, originally without knowing it, for the production of wines and beers and in the baking of leavened bread. Natural wines (those in which no alcohol has been added) contain 13–17 per cent alcohol which is the highest concentration that the yeast cells can endure. As the concentration of alcohol rises, growth of yeast cells is inhibited, and no more alcohol is produced. In the baking industry it is the production of CO_2 that causes the dough to rise.

Yeast cells multiply rapidly by budding or by fission. Baker's yeast (*Saccharomyces cerevisiae*) is a budding yeast (Figure 10·2A). Successive budding results in a chain of yeast cells which is sometimes referred to as a pseudomycelium. *Saccharomyces cerevisiae* is heterothallic. When two compatible cells come into contact under favorable conditions, they fuse and produce a zygote. The diploid cell multiplies by budding and large populations are produced. Eventually, the diploid nucleus undergoes meiosis and the four resultant nuclei become incorporated into four ascospores within the mother cell which is now the ascus

(Figure 11·5). The ascus eventually bursts and liberates the ascospores which begin to bud and form large populations of haploid yeast cells of both mating types.

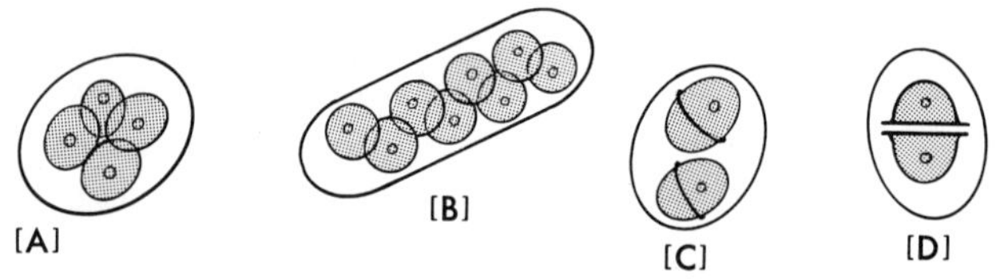

Figure 11·5. Yeast asci containing ascospores. A: Tetrasporous ascus. **B:** Octosporous ascus. **C,D:** Bispored asci.

FILAMENTOUS ASCOMYCETES

The thallus of the filamentous Ascomycetes consists of septate hyphae with chitinous walls. The septa are perforated with a simple pore through the center; protoplasmic strands pass through pores connecting all portions of the mycelium. Nuclei also pass through the septa. The individual compartments or cells are uninucleate in some species, but multinucleate in most Ascomycetes.

Typically, Ascomycetes reproduce asexually by the formation of conidia or special spore-producing hyphae, the **conidiophores.** Conidiophores may be organized in layers lining the inside of a hollow container, the **pycnidium** (plural, **pycnidia**) (Figure 11·6), or on the surface of a mycelial mat, the **acervulus** (plural, **acervuli**) (Figure 11·7), or may be produced singly by the hyphae anywhere on the mycelium (Figure 10·7). Many Ascomycetes, however, reproduce only sexually and depend solely on the ascospores for their propagation. Sexual reproduction typically results in the formation of a spore-fruit, the **ascocarp,** in or on which asci are formed.

There are three general types of ascocarps. The **cleistothecium** (Figure 11·8A,B) is a completely closed structure which typically contains globose asci at various levels. A **perithecium** (Figure 11·8C,D) is a flask-shaped fruiting body provided with a pore at the top, the **ostiole,** through which the ascospores are forcibly liberated. It contains a basal layer of cylindrical or club-shaped asci. An **apothecium** (Figure 11·8E,F) is an open ascocarp bearing an exposed layer of asci. Apothecia may be club-shaped, tongue-shaped, bell-shaped, spongelike, or convoluted. Whatever its shape, the ascocarp is a product of the somatic hyphae which wholly or partially encloses the female sex organ, the **ascogonium,** from which the asci develop following fertilization. The

[A]

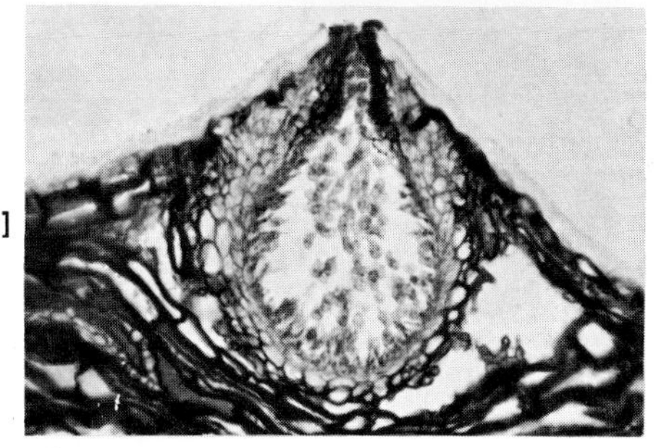
[B]

Figure 11·6. A: Pycnidia as they appear on the surface of a grape leaf. **B:** Cross section of a pycnidium showing conidiophores and conidia. Some conidia are in the process of escaping through the ostiole. [Photos by C. J. Alexopoulos.]

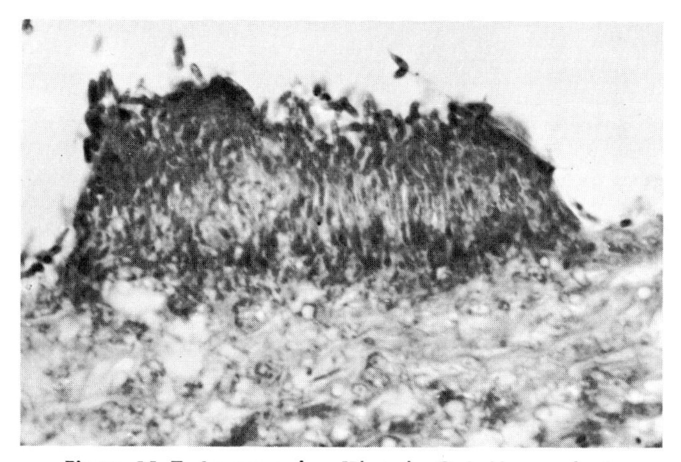

Figure 11·7. An acervulus. [Photo by C. J. Alexopoulos.]

sexual act stimulates the formation of the ascocarp but the chemical mechanism which is responsible for this remains unknown.

The general life cycle of the filamentous Ascomycetes is diagrammed in Figure 11·9. The young mycelium produces conidia which are disseminated, germinate, and produce more mycelium which repeats the asexual cycle. As the mycelium ages it begins to form gametangia. The female organ is a uninucleate or multinucleate ascogonium, often

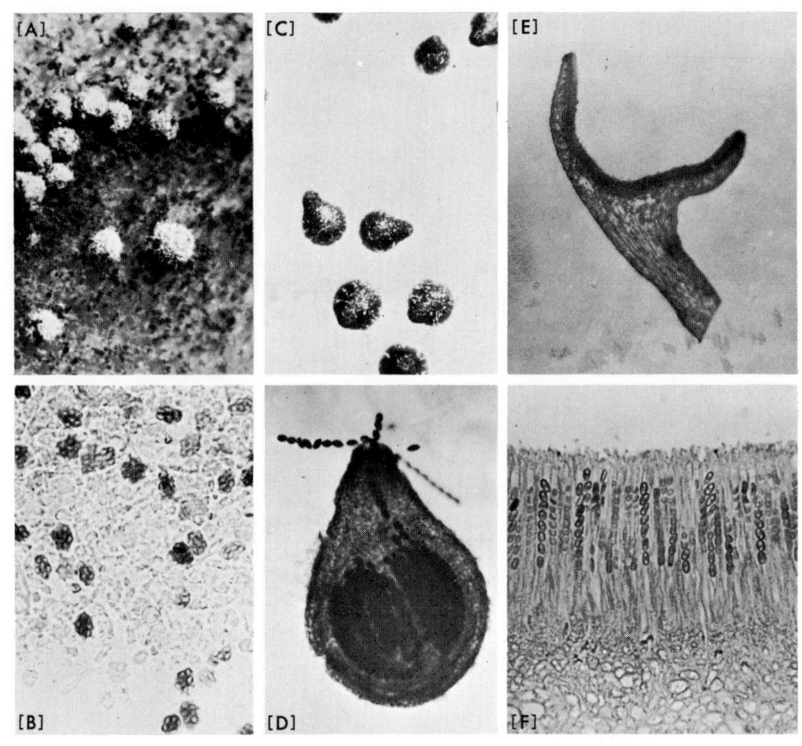

Figure 11·8. Three types of ascocarps. A: Cleistothecia. **B:** Interior of a cleistothecium showing irregular arrangement of the asci. **C:** Perithecia. **D:** Perithecium photographed by transmitted light showing regular arrangement of the asci in a basal layer. **E:** Longitudinal section of an apothecium. **F:** Enlarged view of the apothecial surface showing regular arrangement of the asci in a basal layer. [Photos by C. J. Alexopoulos.]

provided with a receptive hyphal branch, the **trichogyne.** Male sex organs are either antheridia or **spermatia** (singular, **spermatium**). An antheridium attaches itself to an ascogonium (Figure 11·10A) and transfers its nuclei to it when the walls dissolve at the point of contact (Figure 11·10B). Plasmogamy stimulates the somatic hyphae below the ascogonium to produce a protective cover around the sexual apparatus. This protective covering develops into the ascocarp. At the same time, plasmogamy also stimulates the ascogonium to produce a number of buds which elongate into **ascogenous hyphae.** The ascogonial and antheridial nuclei divide once as they pass into the ascogenous hyphae. The latter become septate, and many cells, particularly those located near the tips, contain two nuclei, one from the ascogonium and one from the antheridium (Figure 11·10C). Such a pair of nuclei is called a **dikaryon** (plural, **dikarya**) (Figure 11·10D). The ascogenous hypha bends at the tip and a hook cell is formed (Figure 11·10E). Its

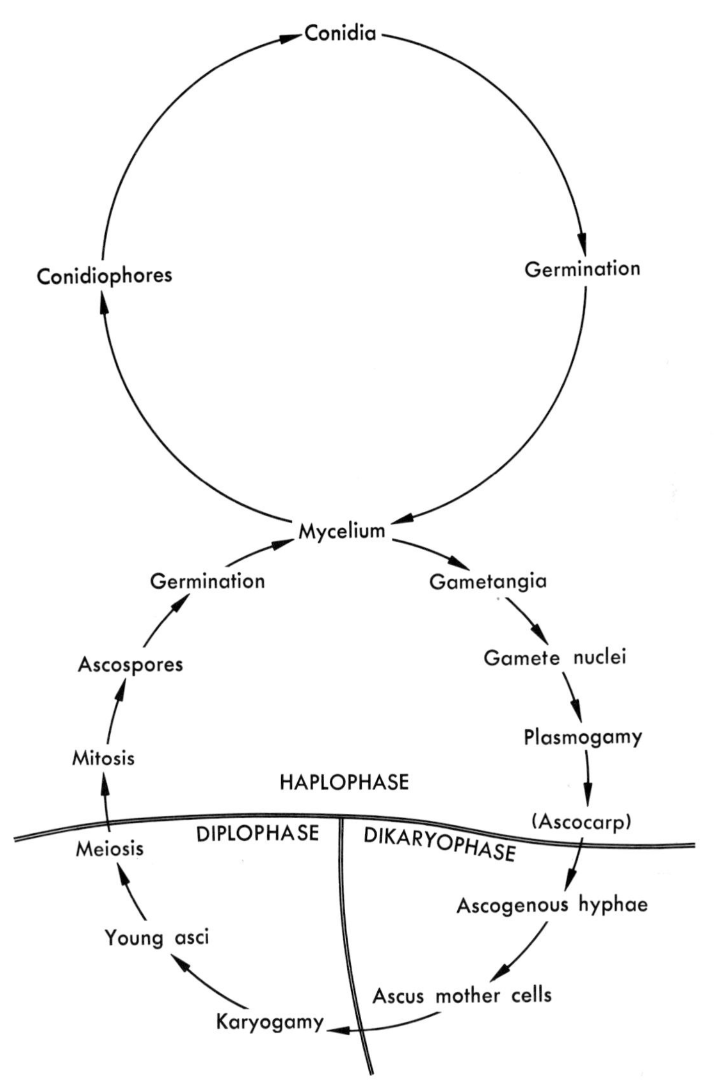

Figure 11·9. Life cycle of the filamentous Ascomycetes. [From C. J. Alexopoulos, *Introductory Mycology*, 2d ed., New York: Wiley, 1962, p. 264.]

nuclei divide, septa are formed, and the penultimate cell of the hook contains a dikaryon. This is the ascus mother-cell which will develop into the ascus (Figurc 11·10F,G). The two nuclei of the ascus mother-cell then fuse (Figure 11·10H). *The resulting zygote nucleus in the young ascus is the only diploid nucleus in the entire life cycle of the filamentous Ascomycetes.* Immediately after karyogamy, meiosis takes place, resulting in the formation of a tetrad (Figure 11·10I,J). The four nuclei thus formed in the ascus either become incorporated into

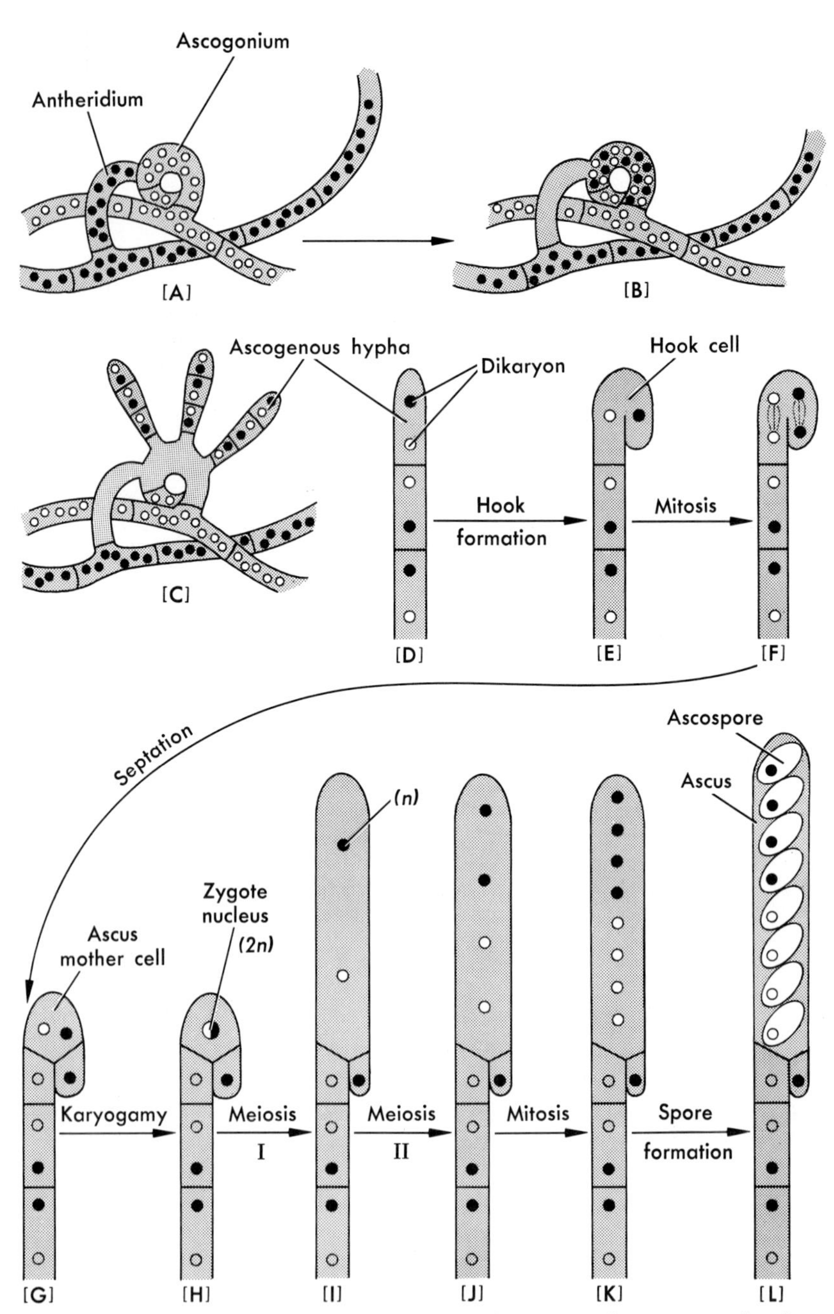

Figure 11·10. Diagrammatic representation of ascus and ascospore development in a heterothallic ascomycete. Filled and unfilled nuclei represent the two compatible mating types.

four ascospores, or, more often, divide once more by mitosis and eight ascospores are subsequently formed, 2 from each nucleus of the tetrad (Figure 11·10K,L). Ascospores are produced by a complex process known as "free cell formation." Not all the cytoplasm in the ascus is utilized in ascospore formation; what is left—the **epiplasm**—is said to function in nourishing the young ascospores, but this is difficult to determine. Figure 11·11 depicts 3 types of asci.

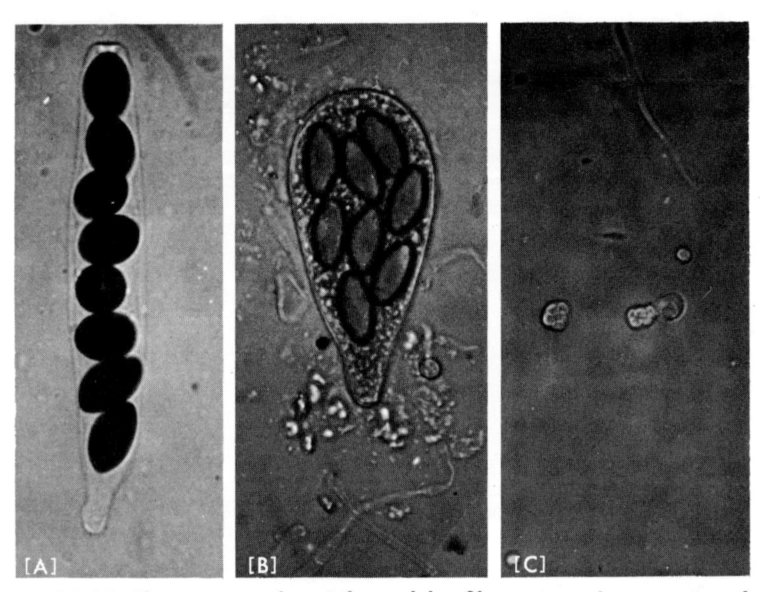

Figure 11·11. Three types of asci formed by filamentous Ascomycetes. A: A cylindrical ascus. **B:** A club-shaped ascus. **C:** Two more or less globose asci. [Photos by C. J. Alexopoulos.]

In Ascomycetes, such as *Neurospora,* which have narrow cylindrical asci, the ascospores are arranged in the same manner as the nuclei of the tetrad, and by isolating them in sequence the experimenter can easily determine how segregation of genetic characters takes place. This is but one of the many reasons why *Neurospora* has been such a useful tool in the study of biochemical genetics.

Class Basidiomycetes

INTRODUCTION

The class Basidiomycetes is a large one encompassing a great variety of fungi which to the uninitiated may appear to be totally unrelated. The rusts, the smuts, the jelly fungi, the bracket fungi, the coral fungi, the mushrooms, the puffballs, the earthstars, the stinkhorns, and the bird's nest fungi are all Basidiomycetes (Figure 11·12). The fruiting bodies of these fungi are but a small part of the total thallus which consists of mycelial hyphae. These grow in the soil, in logs and tree stumps, and in the living plant bodies which some Basidiomycetes parasitize. Among the parasitic Basidiomycetes, the rusts and the smuts have been

Figure 11·12. Fruiting bodies of Basidiomycetes. A: Bracket fungi. **B:** Coral fungi. **C** and **D:** Mushrooms. **E:** Stinkhorns. **F:** Puffballs. [**C** by C. J. Alexopoulos; **F** by H. C. Bold; others courtesy Ruth Allen, F. C. Strong, E. S. Beneke, and H. Aldrich, respectively.]

known since ancient times. The Romans, recognizing the importance of the rust as an economic factor, organized the Robigalia, a festival designed to propitiate the rust god Robigus in the hope they would avert or minimize the effect of the rust on their fields. Various shelf or bracket fungi destroy millions of dollars worth of timber and lumber annually. Jelly fungi are dried and sold for food in the Orient, and in the United States and in Europe a multimillion dollar mushroom-growing industry flourishes.

Just as the ascus is the structure which distinguishes the Ascomycetes from all other fungi, so does the **basidium** (plural, **basidia**) (Figure 11·13) set apart the Basidiomycetes in a class by themselves. A basidium is a structure on which basidiospores are produced following karyogamy and meiosis. Basidiospores are therefore haploid. Ascomycetes produce their ascospores inside an ascus; Basidiomycetes produce basidiospores on the surface of a basidium; but the nuclear history that precedes ascospore and basidiospore formation is essentially the same. This is one reason why many mycologists are convinced that the Basidiomycetes have originated from ascomycetous ancestors. Whether this is true

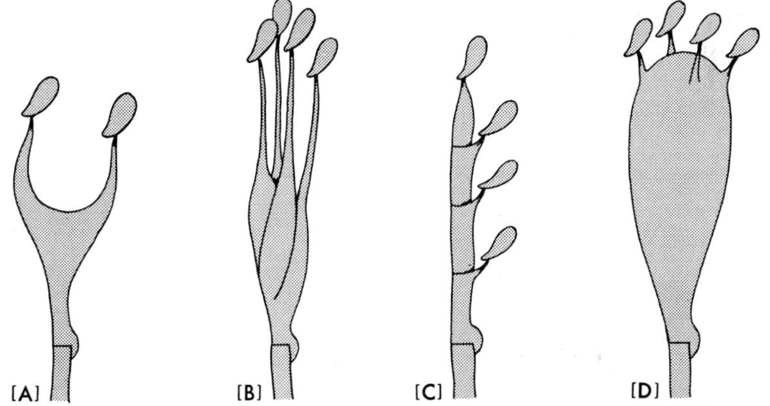

Figure 11·13. Four types of basidia. A, B, and C are basidia encountered in various jelly fungi. D: Basidial type found in mushrooms and related Basidiomycetes.

is, at present, impossible to determine with any degree of certainty.

The spore-bearing bodies (**basidiocarps**) of the Basidiomycetes (Figure 11·12) are among the largest of fungal structures and must have been observed in nature by man as soon as he became cognizant of his environment. A great folklore has been woven around mushrooms in many parts of the world and much has been written about the role that mushrooms have played in man's affairs through the ages. One of the most absorbing accounts is the beautiful two-volume treatise written by Valentina and R. G. Wasson entitled *Mushrooms, Russia and History* which became a collector's item soon after it was published.

GENERAL LIFE CYCLE

The mycelium of the Basidiomycetes passes through two main stages. It begins as primary mycelium when a basidiospore germinates. This type is composed of uninucleate cells and is, consequently, septate. Soon after it is formed the primary mycelium comes into contact with another compatible mycelium with which it exchanges nuclei. The invading nuclei multiply rapidly and migrate from cell to cell through the septa, distributing themselves in such a way so as to render each cell binucleate. Such binucleate cells carry one nucleus from each parent and the nuclear pair in each cell is a dikaryon, comparable to the dikarya in the ascogenous hyphae of the Ascomycetes. As these binucleate hyphae grow, the nuclei divide synchronously, and the new cells formed are always dikaryotic. Thus an extensive secondary, binucleate mycelium is formed. The septa of the Basidiomycete mycelium, in some species that have been investigated, are quite complex. Instead of a simple perforation, each exhibits a perforated swelling enveloped on both sides by a multiperforated membrane (Figure 11·14). This has been termed the **dollipore septum.** Whether it is characteristically present in Basidiomycetes remains to be established.

A feature of the secondary mycelium of many, but not all, Basidiomycetes is the presence of **clamp connections** over the septa.

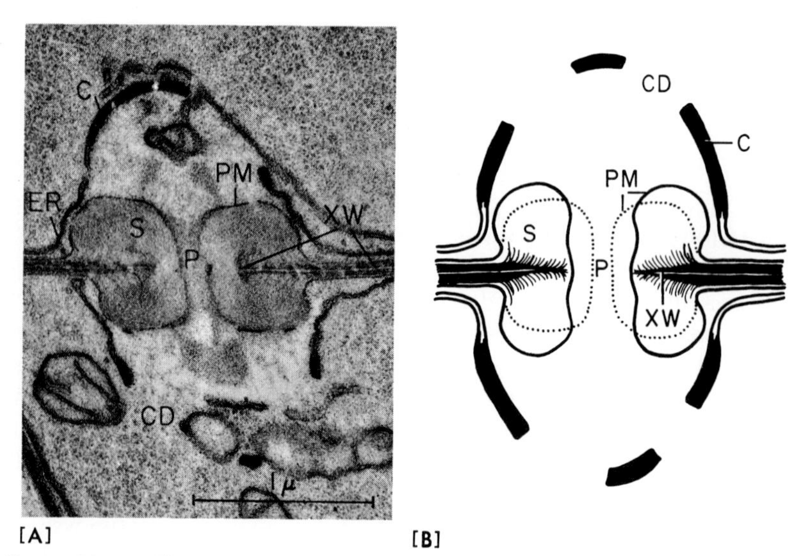

Figure 11·14. The septal pore apparatus (dolipore septum) of some Basidiomycetes. A: Longitudinal section of a hypha of *Rhizoctonia solani* showing cross wall (*XW*), septal swelling (*S*), septal pore (*P*), and septal cap (*C*). **B:** Diagram of the septal pore apparatus in longitudinal section showing it in the normal position (dotted line) and modified during protoplasmic streaming (solid line). [Courtesy E. E. Butler. Reproduced by permission of The Rockefeller University Press from Bracker and Butler, *J. Cell Biol., 21:* 152–157, 1964.]

Clamp connections are hook-like structures (Figure 11·15) which serve to bridge two adjacent cells and which function during cell division as a mechanism thought to insure the perpetuation of the dikaryotic condition and the proper distribution of the two types of nuclei involved. Figure 11·16 illustrates this mechanism.

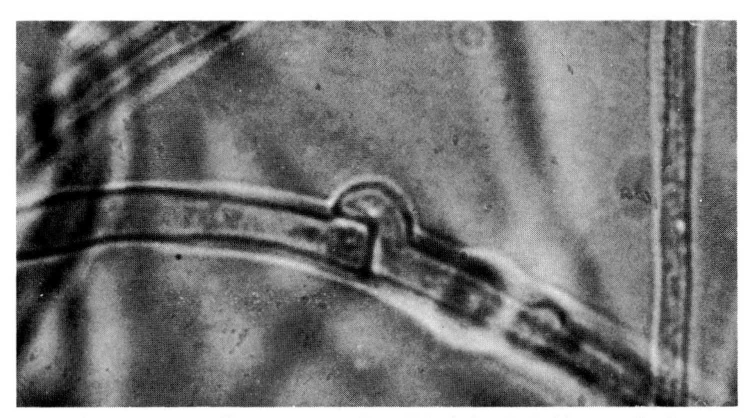

Figure 11·15. Clamp connection. [Photo by C. J. Alexopoulos.]

When the binucleate mycelium reaches a certain stage of maturity, it begins to weave complex tissues which develop into the basidiocarps. Here the basidia are borne in various ways. A basidium begins as a tip cell of a dikaryotic hypha. The nuclei fuse, meiosis takes place, and four nuclei are formed. In the meantime the basidium assumes the shape characteristic of that species and generally produces four pointed protuberances, the **sterigmata** (singular, **sterigma**) at the tips of which the four basidiospores are borne. The four nuclei, the products of meiosis, now migrate toward the sterigmata and squeeze through them, passing into the basidiospores (Figure 11·17). When the basidiospores are mature a gas bubble is formed at the base of each basidiospore and the spore is forcibly released by jet action. Although some Basidiomycetes produce conidia, the majority depend primarily on basidiospores for their propagation and dissemination. Basidiospores are produced in

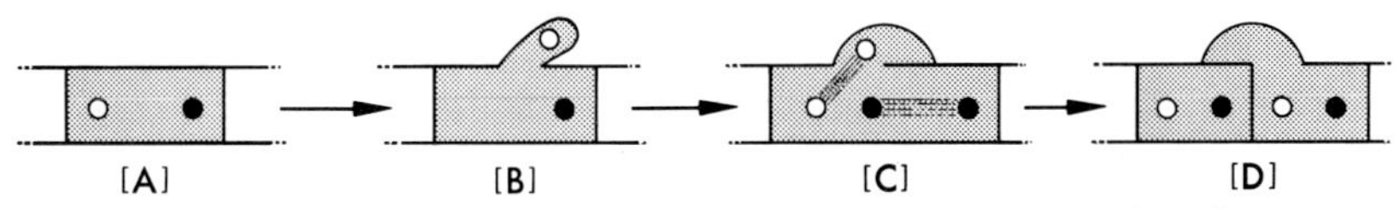

Figure 11·16. Diagrammatic representation of the formation of a clamp connection in a heterothallic basidiomycete. Filled and unfilled nuclei represent two compatible mating types.

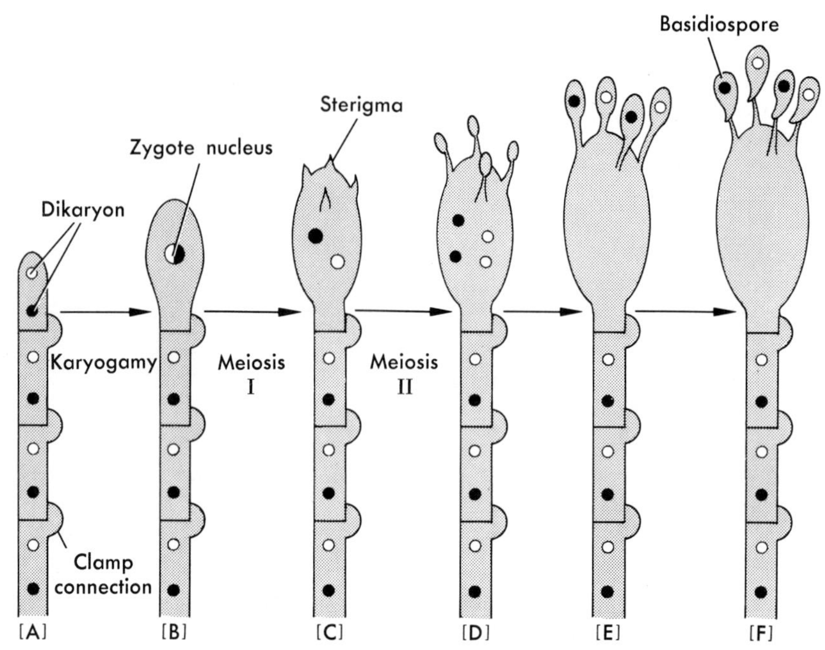

Figure 11·17. Diagrammatic representation of basidial and basidiospore development, without crossing over, in a heterothallic basidiomycete. Filled and unfilled nuclei represent two compatible mating types.

enormous numbers. It has been estimated that several trillion spores may be produced by a single, fairly large basidiocarp.

The life cycle just outlined is typical of the majority of the Basidiomycetes. Note that differentiated sex organs are lacking and that the sexual function has been delegated to the tips of ordinary growing hyphae. Note also that conidia play a secondary role in the life cycle of these organisms.

Basidia are produced in special ways by the basidiocarps of various types of Basidiomycetes. Club and tooth fungi, for example, bear their basidia on the surface of club or tooth-shaped structures; in pore fungi basidia line the inner surface of pores or tubes; mushrooms produce their basidia on the surface of **lamellae** (singular, **lamella**) or gills borne on the under side of umbrella-like fruiting bodies; puffballs, stinkhorns, and related fungi produce their basidia inside closed basidiocarps, the basidia disintegrating by the time the spores are released.

In the ground where the mycelium of many mushrooms normally grows, the hyphae spread out from a central point in all directions forming a circular colony very much as they do in a petri dish in the laboratory. When the mycelium is ready to sporulate, mushrooms are produced at the periphery of the colony thus forming a ring. This is known as a **fairy ring** because of a mediaeval superstition that the mushroom circle represented the path of dancing fairies. Sometimes the ring of mushrooms may be complete; at other times a half-circle or an arc of mushrooms may be formed. When fairy rings appear on grassy lawns, golf courses, or football fields, the grass inside the ring is generally greener than elsewhere because the older hyphae within the ring die and their disintegrating protoplasts release nitrogen into the ground which fertilizes the grass. Fairy rings increase in diameter year after year if the ground in which they grow remains undisturbed. Some fairy rings are known to be more than 400 years old.

Many of the 10,000 or more kinds of mushrooms are edible; a few are poisonous, and some of the latter are deadly. Among the latter are the destroying angel (*Amanita verna*) and the death cup (*Amanita phalloides*). The fly mushroom (*Amanita muscaria*) is also very poisonous if consumed in any quantity. It should be emphasized here that there is no known test, except eating a mushroom, to determine whether it is edible or poisonous. One must learn to identify mushrooms before he collects them for food. Mushrooms grown commercially are safe, but wild mushrooms offered for sale may not be if the person who picked them was not an expert in selecting them. Even so, it must be borne in mind that individuals differ in their susceptibility to mushroom poisons. The old dictum "one man's meat is another man's poison" is particularly applicable here.

Some mushrooms contain hallucinogenic substances which produce ecstatic effects when the mushrooms are consumed. Such are the "sacred mushrooms" of Mexico which have been used by certain Mexican Indians for centuries in their religious rites. In recent years a thorough study has been made of these mushrooms and the hallucinogenic principles have been isolated and one of them synthesized. They are being used experimentally in the study of certain types of mental illness.

THE RUSTS

The rusts are obligate parasites attacking a great variety of plants. Their life cycles are very complex, consisting of several distinctly recognizable phases produced in regular sequence. Many rust fungi are **autoecious**—that is, they complete their entire life cycle on a single species of host. Asparagus rust is an example. A large number of rusts on the other hand are **heteroecious** requiring two entirely different and unrelated host species in order to complete their life cycle. The primary mycelium of heteroecious rusts grows on one host and the secondary mycelium on the other. The best known example of a heteroecious rust is *Puccinia graminis,* the cause of black stem rust of wheat and other grains. The alternate host of *P. graminis* is the common barberry *Berberis vulgaris*.

Rusts are the only Basidiomycetes which produce differentiated sex organs; male spermatia borne in flask-shaped structures (**spermogonia**) (Figure 11·18) and female **receptive hyphae** generally borne in the vicinity of the spermogonia by the primary mycelium. When the sex organs are mature, the spermatia exude in a droplet of sweet, fragrant nectar from the orifice of the spermogonium. This attracts flies and

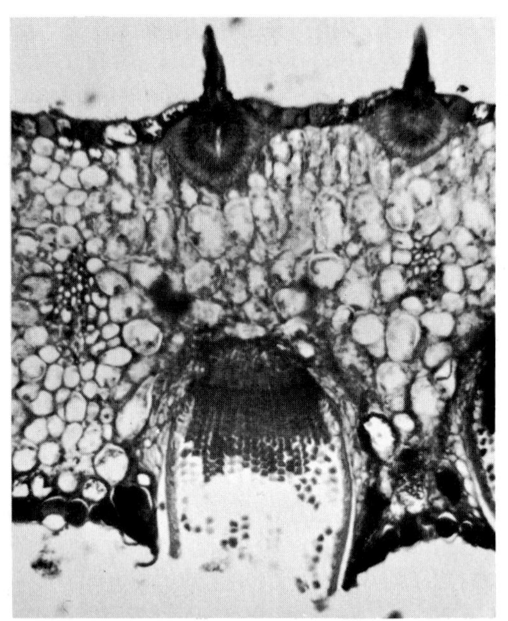

Figure 11·18. *Puccinia graminis.* Cross section of a barberry leaf showing two spermogonia on the upper side and an aecium with aeciospores on the lower. [Photo by C. J. Alexopoulos.]

other insects which sip the nectar. As they wander over the host, they carry spermatia to the receptive hyphae thus initiating the sexual cycle.

The primary mycelium of *P. graminis* grows intercellularly in the leaves and stems of the barberry plant, nourishing itself by means of its haustoria. It produces spermogonia and receptive hyphae which protrude from the upper epidermis of the leaf. A short time after the spermatia have been transferred to the receptive hyphae, cuplike structures (**aecia,** singular, **aecium**) appear on the lower side of the leaf (Figure 11·18). They contain binucleate **aeciospores.** These are released and blown by the wind to the wheat fields. On the surface of the wheat plant they germinate and produce binucleate hyphae which penetrate and grow intercellularly. This binucleate mycelium soon produces masses of spiny, binucleate spores (**uredospores**) (Figure 11·19A) which break out through the epidermis of the wheat stalks or leaves in the form of red pustules. Heavily infected plants look as if they are covered with iron rust. So many uredospores are produced, that a person walking through a rusted wheat field will have his clothes covered with a reddish dust. This stage is responsible for the common name of "rust fungi" given to this group of parasites. The uredospores are capable of reinfecting the wheat and may be thought of as being the conidia of the rust fungus. They are carried by the wind over long distances and are mainly responsible for the spread of the rust from plant to plant and from field to field. As the wheat plants ripen, the same pustules which produced the uredospores begin to form yet another type of binucleate spore, the **teliospore** or teleutospore (Figure 11·19B). The teliospores of *Puccinia graminis* are two-celled. Soon after they are formed, the two nuclei in each cell fuse into one diploid nucleus. Teliospores are thick-walled and remain dormant throughout the winter months. In the spring they germinate. A short tube (the **promycelium**) issues from each cell of the teliospore and the diploid

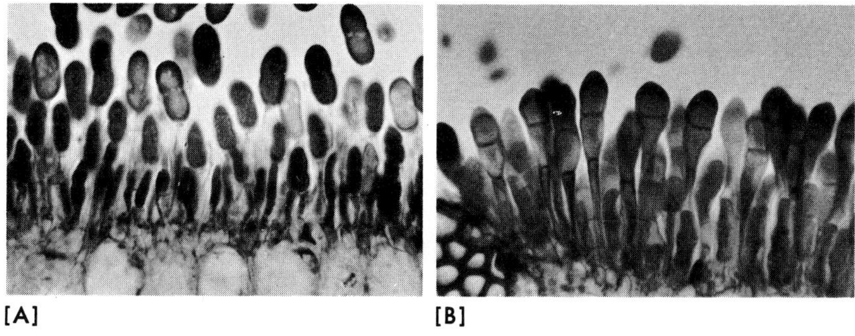

[A] [B]

Figure 11·19. ***Puccinia graminis.*** **A: A mass of one-celled uredospores B: A group of two-celled teliospores. [Photos by C. J. Alexopoulos.]**

nucleus migrates into it. Meiosis now takes place and the four resulting nuclei become evenly distributed in the promycelium. Septa are now laid down which render the promycelium four-celled. Each of these cells soon produces a basidiospore on the tip of a sterigma and the 4 nuclei pass into the 4 basidiospores. Since *Puccinia graminis* is heterothallic, two of the basidiospores are of one mating type (+) and two are of the other (−). Thus the basidial apparatus of the rusts consists of the teliospore, in which karyogamy takes place, and the promycelium, in which meiosis occurs.

The basidiospores are discharged forcibly and are carried by air currents. They are unable to parasitize the wheat plant and can establish a primary mycelium only in a barberry plant. Those that reach barberry plants carry on the life cycle of the rust; the others perish. This is why eradication of the barberry plant helps control wheat rust.

The Fungi Imperfecti

Fungi Imperfecti, also called Deuteromycetes—meaning secondary fungi—are fungi which mostly resemble Ascomycetes, or, in a few instances, Basidiomycetes, but which are known to produce neither asci nor basidia. They propagate by conidia which are very similar to those produced by many well-known Ascomycetes (or Basidiomycetes) and are therefore believed to be Ascomycetes (or Basidiomycetes) which have lost their ability to reproduce sexually. Many Fungi Imperfecti are known to possess a parasexual cycle in which hyphal union, nuclear fusion, and haploidization (reduction of the amount of chromatin from the diploid to the haploid condition) occur, but not in a definite place or at a definite time in the life cycle. Although the parasexual cycle has some of the genetic advantages of a true sexual cycle, it is much less efficient and does not result in the production of spore fruits (ascocarps or basidiocarps) or meiospores (ascospores or basidiospores).

Many thousands of species of Fungi Imperfecti are known. A large number of these are of great economic importance. *Penicillium chrysogenum* is the source of penicillin; *Penicillium roqueforti* and *Penicillium camemberti* are used in the manufacture of blue cheese and camembert cheese respectively; *Septoria apii* is the cause of late blight of celery; *Cercospora apii* causes a destructive celery leaf spot and may be a serious human pathogen as well; *Alternaria solani* causes early blight of potatoes.

CHAPTER

12

Algae and Fungi of the Past

Fossil Algae

THE FOSSIL RECORD of algae, both direct and indirect, is a long one, extending back into the Pre-Cambrian (Table 12·1, page 120). The abundance of limestone, composed of calcium carbonate, suggests intensive and extensive activity of photosynthetic organisms in ancient seas—carbonates precipitated as they removed carbon dioxide from soluble bicarbonates. Extant algae in hot springs (blue-green algae) and in oceans (various green and red corraline algae) are currently carrying on just such activities, as are some of the calcareous stoneworts —for example, *Chara* species of fresh and brackish waters.

The recent studies of Barghoorn and his associates on the biota of the Gunflint Chert in Pre-Cambrian formations on the north shore of Lake Superior have revealed an impressive collection of algal remains, approximately 1,900,000,000 years old. The organisms (Figure 12·1) seem to have been members of both the Cyanophycophyta and Chlorophycophyta. Examination of successively younger strata of sedimentary rocks has revealed the occurrence of an increasingly diverse algal flora, representatives of which have persisted to the present without profound modification. Thus, calcareous blue-green, green, red algae and the stoneworts became significant in the flora in Devonian times (Table 12·1, page 121) and well-preserved fossil specimens have been recovered. Especially striking are widespread tubular green algae (Figure 12·2) in which the pattern of organization is essentially similar to that of modern genera. Also in Ordovician strata occur the first remains of Pyrrophyta (dinoflagellates) which increased in abundance in the

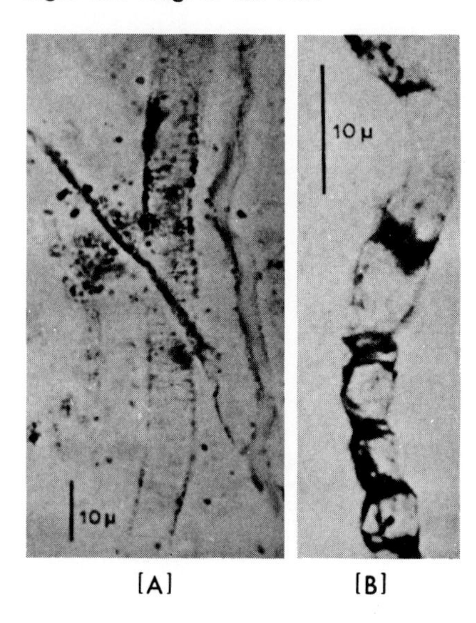

Figure 12·1. Pre-Cambrian algae. A: *Animikiea septata,* somewhat similar to living *Oscillatoria.* **B:** *Gunflintia grandis,* possibly a green alga like *Ulothrix.* [After E. S. Barghoorn and S. A. Tyler, in *Science 147:* 563–577, 1965.]

Mesozoic through the present. Fossil Charophyta (Figure 12·3A) are also abundant.

Bacillariophycophyta (diatoms) with their siliceous frustules (Figure 12·3B) are especially well adapted to preservation as fossils, and their record extends back probably into the Jurassic but certainly to the Cretaceous. Great deposits of diatom frustules, both fresh-water

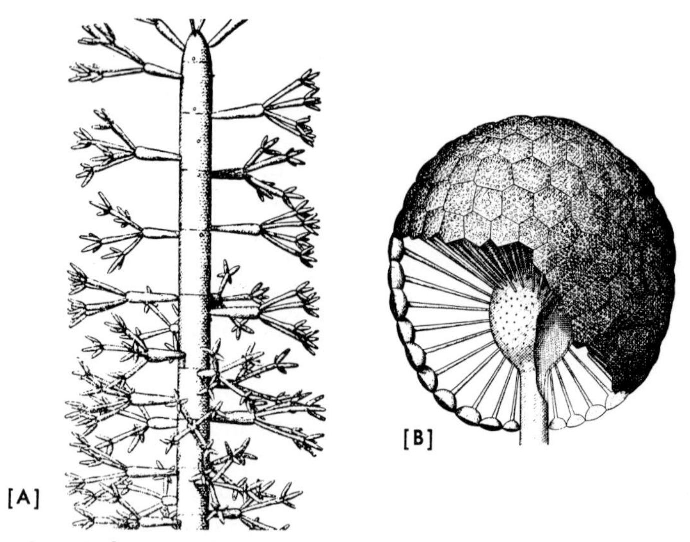

Figure 12·2. Ordovician algae. A: *Primicorralina trentonensis.* **B:** *Goniolina geometrica,* both calcareous algae. [**B** from J. Pia, *Die Siphoneae verticillatae von Karbon bis zur Kreide,* Abh. Zool.-bot. Ges. Bd. 11, H Z Wien, 1920.]

and marine, have accumulated and are quarried or mined as diatomaceous earth. Perhaps the most famous bed is at Lompoc, California, where the exposed deposit extends in some places 1,400 feet vertically for an area about twelve miles square. Large numbers of diatom frustules are accumulating currently in a number of Florida lakes.

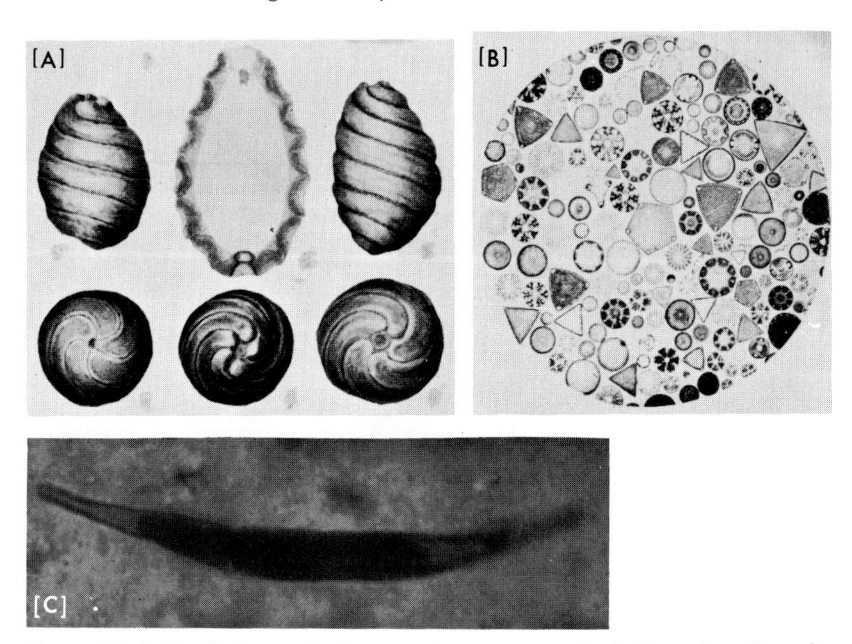

Figure 12·3. Fossil algae. A: Oospores (mature zygotes) of *Charophyta* from the Pennsylvanian (compare with Figure 6·18). **B:** Fossil diatoms from Hungary. **C:** *Paleoclosterium leptum,* a fossil desmid (compare with Figure 6·13A). [**A** from R. E. Peck and J. A. Eyer, in *J. Paleont. 37:* 835–844, 1963; **B** from A. Mann, "The Economic Importance of the Diatoms," Annual Report of the Smithsonian Institution, 1916; **C** from R. A. Baschnagel, in *Trans. Amer. Micr. Soc. 85:* 297–302, 1966.]

The Chrysophycophyta are first represented in significant abundance in the Cretaceous. The fossil record of the Phaeophycophyta is fragmentary; *Fucus*-like specimens have been described from the Paleozoic. Calcareous Rhodophycophyta have been reported from the Mesozoic (Triassic) through more recent strata.

The noncalcareous algae apparently have not been preserved as fossils to any great extent.

However, ten genera with twenty-two species of noncalcareous algae (Figure 12·4) have been described from Miocene (Table 12·1, page 121) strata in Los Angeles County, California. These include a siphonalean green alga, various brown algae, including a kelp, and representatives of several orders of red algae; none of these was identical with extant species.

TABLE 12·1
Geologic Time

ERA	SYSTEM OR PERIOD	SERIES OR EPOCH	ESTIMATED AGES OF TIME BOUNDARIES (millions of years)
Cenozoic	Quaternary	Recent	
		Pleistocene	1.5
	Tertiary	Pliocene	12
		Miocene	25
		Oligocene	34
		Eocene	60
		Paleocene	64
Mesozoic	Cretaceous	Upper (Late)	
		Lower (Early)	132
	Jurassic	Upper (Late)	
		Middle (Middle)	180
		Lower (Early)	
	Triassic	Upper (Late)	
		Middle (Middle)	225
		Lower (Early)	

	Permian			275
	Carboniferous	Pennsylvanian	Upper (Late) Middle (Middle) Lower (Early)	310
		Mississippian	Upper (Late) Lower (Early)	350
	Devonian		Upper (Late) Middle (Middle) Lower (Early)	405
Paleozoic	Silurian		Upper (Late) Middle (Middle) Lower (Early)	430
	Ordovician		Upper (Late) Middle (Middle) Lower (Early)	485
	Cambrian		Upper (Late) Middle (Middle) Lower (Early)	600
	Pre-Cambrian			4,500

Our knowledge of fossil algae is admittedly incomplete and fragmentary, but it is clear that algae are very ancient in their origins and that extant representatives have not changed markedly from their ancient precursors. As a result, the fossil record is not helpful in elucidating the major pathways of algal evolution.

Figure 12·4. ***Julescraneia grandicornis*, a Miocene kelp.** [From B. C. Parker and E. Y. Dawson, in *Nova Hedwigia 10*: 273–295, 1965.]

Fossil Fungi

Paleontological studies indicate that the fungi as well as the algae are a very ancient group, probably extending back into the Pre-Cambrian although the supposed fossil fungi of that era cannot be unquestionably identified as such. Most undisputed fungal remains date from the Devonian on. By the end of the Paleozoic all the major fungal groups are represented in the fossil record and many specimens can be placed in well-known modern genera. Not only hyphae, but various types of reproductive organs have been found and, in at least a few cases, there is enough well-preserved material to enable us to reconstruct the entire life cycle of a fossil fungus.

Many of the best preserved fungi were epiphyllous (Figure 12·5). There is no way to determine with certainty whether they were parasitic. However, in a few specimens, hyphal organs have been found which are undoubted haustoria, indicating a parasitic habit of the fungi which possessed them. In a recent extensive study of fungi from the Eocene deposits of western Tennessee, Dilcher found that some of the fungi were always associated with leaves of specific hosts whereas others showed no host specificity. This is, of course, exactly the situation that exists with living fungi today.

It is of further interest to record here that well-preserved specimens of what are unquestionably fossil mycorrhizae have been discovered in

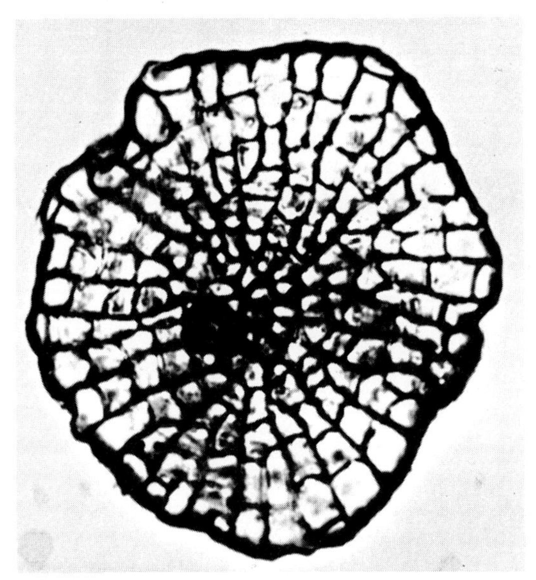

Figure 12·5. A fossil epiphyllous fungus (*Calimothallus pertusus*) from the Eosine. [Reproduced by permission from D. L. Dilcher, in *Palaeontographica, 116:* 1–54, 1965.]

coal balls. This suggests that the apparently mutually beneficial relationship between the roots of some green plants and some fungi is of ancient origin. On the other hand, fossil lichens are rare indeed, but a few specimens which are accepted as true lichens have been found in amber deposits in Germany.

So many of the fossil fungi resemble living forms in their essential morphology that the fossil record is unfortunately of little help in determining the origin and relationships of the modern species. Nevertheless, much remains to be done and it is not impossible that some clues to the evolution of the fungi will yet be gleaned from the fossil remains.

Selected References

Algae

Chapman, V. J. *Seaweeds and Their Uses.* London: Methuen and Co., Ltd., 1950.

Chapman, V. J. *The Algae.* London: Macmillan and Co., Ltd., 1962. New York: St Martin's Press, 1962.

Chase, F. M. *Useful Algae.* Washington, D.C.: Smithsonian Institution, Publication 3667, 1941.

Christensen, T. *Alger* (Bot. Syst. Bot.), Vol. II. Munksgaard, 1962.

Conger, P. S. *Significance of Shell Structure in Diatoms.* Washington, D.C.: Smithsonian Institution, Smithsonian Report, 1936, pp. 325–344.

Dawson, E. Y. *How to Know the Seaweeds.* Dubuque, Iowa: Wm. C. Brown Company, 1956.

Dawson, E. Y. *Marine Botany.* New York: Holt, Rinehart and Winston, Inc., 1966.

Fritsch, F. E. *Structure and Reproduction of the Algae,* Vols. 1 and 2. New York: Cambridge University Press, 1935 and 1945.

Jackson, D. F. *Algae and Man.* New York: Plenum Press, 1964.

Krauss, R. W. "Mass Culture of Algae for Food and Other Organic Compounds." *Amer. J. Bot., 49:* 425–435, 1962.

Lewin, R. A. (ed.). *Physiology and Biochemistry of Algae.* New York and London: Academic Press, 1962.

Newton, L. *Seaweed Utilization.* Sampson Low, 1951.

Palmer, C. M. *Algae in Water Supplies.* Washington, D.C.: Public Health Service Publication No. 657. (88 pp.) 1959.

Papenfuss, G. F. *Classification of the Algae*. Century Progress Nat. Sci. 1853–1953 (pp. 115–224). San Francisco: California Academy of Sciences, 1955.

Prescott, G. W. *Algae of the Western Great Lakes Area,* 2nd ed. Bloomfield Hills, Mich.: Cranbrook Institute of Science Press, Bulletin 31, 1966.

Prescott, G. W. *How to Know the Fresh-Water Algae*. Dubuque, Iowa: Wm. C. Brown Company, 1954.

Pringsheim, E. G. *Pure Cultures of Algae, Their Preparation and Maintenance*. New York: Cambridge University Press, 1946.

Round, F. C. *The Biology of the Algae*. New York: St. Martin's Press, 1965.

Scagel, R. F., R. J. Bandoni, G. E. Rouse, W. B. Schofield, J. R. Stein, and T. M. C. Taylor. *An Evolutionary Survey of the Plant Kingdom*. Belmont, Calif.: Wadsworth Publishing Co., 1965.

Smith, G. M. *Marine Algae of the Monterey Peninsula*. Stanford, Calif.: Stanford University Press, 1944.

Smith, G. M. *Freshwater Algae of the United States*. New York: McGraw-Hill Book Co., 1950.

Smith, G. M. *Cryptogamic Botany*. Vol. 1, New York: McGraw-Hill Book Co., 1955.

Smith, G. M. (ed.). *Manual of Phycology*. Waltham, Mass.: Chronica Botanica Co., 1951.

Starr, R. C. "The Culture Collection of Algae at Indiana University," *Amer. J. Bot., 51:* 1013–1044, 1964.

Taylor, W. R. *Marine Algae of the Northeastern Coast of North America*. Ann Arbor: University of Michigan Press, 1937.

Taylor, W. R. *Marine Algae of the Eastern Tropical and Subtropical Coasts of the Americas*. Ann Arbor: University of Michigan Press, 1960.

Tiffany, L. H. *Algae, the Grass of Many Waters*. Springfield, Ill.: Charles C. Thomas, 1958.

Tilden, J. E. *The Algae and Their Life Relations*. Minneapolis: University of Minnesota Press, 1935.

Fungi

GENERAL

Ainsworth, G. C. and A. S. Sussman (eds.). *The Fungi*. Vols. I, II. New York: Academic Press, 1965, 1966. (Vol. III in press.)

Alexopoulos, C. J. *Introductory Mycology,* 2nd ed. New York: John Wiley & Sons, 1962.

Bessey, E. A. *Morphology and Taxonomy of Fungi*. Philadelphia: Blakiston Co., 1950.

Christensen, Clyde M. *The Molds and Man,* 2nd ed. Minneapolis: University of Minnesota Press, 1961.

Gray, W. D. *The Relation of Fungi to Human Affairs*. New York: Henry Holt and Co., 1959.

Kavaler, Lucy. *Mushrooms, Molds, and Miracles.* New York: John Day Co., 1965.
Large, E. C. *The Advance of the Fungi.* New York: Henry Holt and Co., 1940.
Ramsbottom, J. *Mushrooms and Toadstools.* London: Collins, 1953.

SPECIAL TOPICS

Cochrane, V. W. *The Physiology of Fungi.* New York: John Wiley & Sons, 1958.
Duddington, C. L. *The Friendly Fungi,* London: Faber and Faber, 1957 (distributed by The Macmillan Co., New York).
Emmons, C. W., C. H. Binford, and J. P. Utz. *Medical Mycology.* Philadelphia: Lea and Febiger, 1963.
Harley, J. L. *The Biology of Mycorrhiza.* London: Leonard Hill, 1959.
Hesler, L. R. *Mushrooms of the Great Smokies.* Knoxville: University of Tennesee Press, 1960.
Ingold, C. T. *Spore Liberation.* Oxford, England: Clarendon Press, 1965.
Kelley, A. P. *Mycotrophy in Plants.* Waltham, Mass.: Chronica Botanica Co., 1950.
Parkinson, D., and J. S. Waid. *The Ecology of Soil Fungi.* Liverpool: Liverpool University Press, 1960.
Smith, A. H. *The Mushroom Hunter's Field Guide,* 2nd ed. Ann Arbor: University of Michigan Press, 1963.
Wasson, Valentina P., and R. G. Wasson. *Mushrooms, Russia, and History,* Vols. I and II. New York: Pantheon Books, 1957.

SLIME MOLDS

Alexopoulos, C. J. "The Myxomycetes II," *Botan. Rev. 29:* 1–78, 1963.
Alexopoulos, C. J., and J. L. Koevenig. *Slime Molds and Research.* B. S. C. S. pamphlet No. 13. American Institute of Biological Sciences. Boston: D. C. Heath and Company, 1963.
Bonner, J. T. *The Cellular Slime Molds.* Princeton, N.J.: Princeton University Press, 1959.
Crowder, W. "Marvels of Mycetozoa," *Nat'l. Geographic 49* (4): 421–443, 1926.
Koevenig, J. L. (Technical Director). *Slime Molds I, II, III.* Color-sound films. Iowa City: University of Iowa, Bureau of Audio-Visual Instruction, Extension Division, 1961.
Martin, G. W. "The Myxomycetes," *Botan. Rev. 6:* 356–388, 1940.

LICHENS

Ahmadjian, V. "Lichens," *Ann. Rev. Microbiol. 19:* 1–20, 1965.
Ahmadjian, V. "Lichens," in S. M. Henry (ed.) *Symbiosis,* Vol. I, pp. 35–97. New York: Academic Press, 1966.
Hale, M. E. Jr. *Lichen Handbook.* Washington, D.C.: Smithsonian Institution, 1961.

FOSSIL FUNGI

Dilcher, D. L. "Epiphyllous Fungi from Eocene Deposits in Western Tennessee, U. S. A.," *Paleontographica 116, Abt. B.:* 1–54, 26 pls., 1965.

Wolf, F. A., and F. T. Wolf. *The Fungi,* Vol. 2. New York: John Wiley & Sons, 1947.

Index

Page numbers in **boldface** type refer to illustrations.